The Daily Telegraph

Book of Word Games

Compiled by Kate Mepham

PAN BOOKS
In association with *The Daily Telegraph*

First published 2008 by Pan Books
an imprint of Pan Macmillan Ltd
Pan Macmillan, 20 New Wharf Road, London N1 9RR
Basingstoke and Oxford

Associated companies throughout the world
www.panmacmillan.com
In association with *The Daily Telegraph*

ISBN: 978 0 330 46429 1

9 8 7 6 5 4 3 2 1

A CIP catalogue record for this book is available from the British Library.

Image-setting and design by Alex Ware, Frome, Somerset

Printed and bound in Great Britain by
CPI Mackays, Chatham ME5 8TD

Contents

Letter Logic

There are no clues to this word puzzle other than the number of squares in the grid and the length of the words or phrases. Use your powers of logic and the given word-list to complete the grid.

1

ALOE
BALLOON
BASIS
BEAR
BEEF
BEETROOT
BODICE
BOMBE
BOOST
CLOVE
CORSAGE
DEAR
DECORATE
EASTERN
EGOISM
ENQUIRE
ESPY
GRASS
GURU
HINDU
INSPIRE
ISLE
LUNCH
MILLER
MINI
NOSE
OAR
ONE
OOZE
OUGHT
PASTE
PRIVATE
QUARTER
RESTORE
ROMANCE
ROTARY
SCORCHED
SCREE
SCULL
SERIOUS
SESAME
SHAMPOO
SHOE
SICK
SIEVE
SKATE
SNIDE
SPELL
SPIKE
SPINE
SPOOR
STORE
SWEAT
SWEETPEA
TALLBOY
TASTE
TROTTER
WARMTH
WARRIOR
WRESTLED
YOUTHFUL
ZEBRA

1

2

AIRCRAFT
ANGRY
ARGUE
ATHENS
ATLAS
AWRY
BARRACKS
BEAR
BLISS
BORDERS
CATCH
CAVIAR
CHILD
COKE
CRASS
CURRY
EXCESS
FAILURE
FEATHER
FIBRE
FLOP
FOSTER
HUT
IDEA
ISLE
LEAK
LINSEED
NATURAL
PACT
PATHETIC
PENCE
PHYSICAL
PLACARD
POST
PRINT
PULSE
REGULAR
RELISH
REPHRASE
RUFFIAN
RUSH
SALTS
SARDINE
SECT
SERVE
SHABBY
SHEEP DIP
SHINE
SIREN
SMELL
SPIKE
SPONSOR
STAIR
STAMINA
STONE
STORM
SUPREME
SWEATER
TAR
TOTEM
TREMOLO
VETO

2

3

ABHOR
ADMIRE
AGENT
AIMED
AMBO
APRON
AUDEN
BANANA
BARN
BEEKEEPER
CHEST
CHOICE
CLAMMY
COMPASS
CRIMINAL
CROWBAR
CRUMPET
DIGS
DISTRACT
DOORSTEP
EARPLUG
EGYPT
FIANCÉE
FUR
GUT
HEXAGRAM
HIKER
HOPE
HOSIERY
IDLE
IMPS
INCLINE
LACE
LESSEE
LITRE
LUPIN
MACAW
MARTINI
MORTISE
NORTH
NOTARY
NOVA
OCEAN
ODOUR
PACKAGE
PARISH
PAST
PATCH
POLO
PREP
RETHINK
ROTUND
SACKS
SLUMBER
SNAIL
SQUAT
STAR
STICK
STUB
TABOO
TAROT
TAWNY
THUMB
TIGER
TINY
TOMBOLA
UNTRUTH
VET
VISOR
YODEL
YOU
YOUNG

3

4

ACORN
ADVERB
AIRFORCE
ALREADY
ATHEIST
BAPTIST
BYPASS
CAT
DEAN
DRAIN
DREGS
DUCHESS
EARL
EASED
EAST
EJECT
EMMENTAL
ENTHUSE
FAT
HEATHER
HOOP
IRONY
ITCH
LENS
LIAR
MANDARIN
MINCE
MULLED
OBVIOUS
ODDS
OPEN
ORCHARD
OVERFED
PICOT
PIRANHA
PLATYPUS
PROSPECT
RIVAL
ROBIN
SALTY
SATIN
SHAFT
SHAWL
SHEEN
SHORTEST
SISAL
SLIME
SNOUT
SOLO
SPRAT
SURLY
SUSHI
TAPIOCA
TOAD
TRENDY
UNHOOK
UPSTART
UTILITY
YACHT
YARDAGE
YELLED
YOYO

4

5

ACRE
ALPHA
APTLY
BAGPIPE
BATHROOM
CATCH
CHIP
CIRCA
COTTAGE
CRAZY
CROCHET
DEPRIVE
DOOM
ENCHANT
ENVIOUS
EYEBROW
FLAGPOLE
FLESH
FLIT
HAT
HERB
IBEX
IMPACT
INFANTRY
INTRO
JACKET
JUPITER
LIMBO
MATCH
MOROCCO
MOSS
MOTTO
NINETEEN
OCTUPLE
PASSWORD
PICASSO
PRINT
RASH
RASP
RAVEN
RELISH
ROTATE
RUSTY
SAVE
SAYSO
SCORE
SCUT
SEPIA
SEVER
SILLY
SOBER
STAVE
STOW
SWARM
SWATHE
TEACAKE
TEARFUL
TIN
TOMATOES
TOTALLY
VALUE
YELLOW

5

6

AGREE
ALE
ANGER
ANIMATE
ANTENNA
ASLEEP
ASTHMA
ATOM
AUSTRIA
BEVERAGE
BUILD
CABIN
CHABLIS
COAL
COCOA
COG
CORKS
CRASS
CUE
CUSTARD
DACE
DEGREE
DINGO
EDAM
ELDER
ELEPHANT
ELEVEN
ERASE
FAST
FEARLESS
FEAST
HASTE
KNIFE
LADY
LOSER
LUSH
MARE
MATRON
MIRACLE
MITRE
MOCHA
NEAR
NINEPIN
NUTTY
OMEN
PAPER
PEAR
PROP
PSYCHE
RAMPANT
RARE
RATRACE
ROGUE
SACHET
SCREAM
SCREECH
SHARD
SMART
SNAKE
SOMME
SPLUTTER
STAG
STARTLE
STILL
TARPAULIN
TEASE
TEMPEST
TERRIER
TIARA
TOY
TRAINEE
TROUT

6

7

ADORE
ALGA
ARID
BATHE
BOMBAST
BRAINY
BRIGADIER
BYTE
CANNON
CAUTIOUS
CEREAL
CHARGE
CHRONIC
CRUSH
CYST
DARLING
DARWIN
DECENCY
DRENCH
DULL
EBB
ERNE
ESPIONAGE
ETHER
ETON
EWE
FOREST
GRAVE
HUTCH
ICECREAM
INANITY
INSTEP
LONDON
LUDO
MATHS
MESSAGE
MOONSTONE
NIGHT
OBTUSE
ONE
PANTOMIME
PARABLE
PENCIL
PIP
POLIO
PREFECT
RAGE
ROBE
RUSTIC
SCAN
SEWN
SHOP
SKILL
SLOE
SLUG
SMIRK
SPANIEL
SPOIL
STARBOARD
SUNNY
TASTING
TELEVISED
THISTLE
VINYL
WASTE
WINCE
ZINC

7

8

AFIRE
AMNESTY
AMPS
ANTHEM
BACTERIA
BAGEL
BEING
BROWN
BUS
CHINA
CLIP
COBALT
DIRT
EAGLE
EASY
EGGS
ENIGMA
EUROPE
FEATHER
FETE
GALA
GLISTENED
GRAPE
HIDE
HIFI
HOLY
HOWEVER
ICING
IGNITED
INTRICATE
KHAKI
LASAGNE
LOAFER
LONELY
MALLET
MANATEE
MARBLE
MOBILE
NAIL
NEWSPAPER
OBSTACLE
OSTEOPATH
PANCAKE
PEST
PLATE
RUG
SCRAP
SEASONS
SEED
SHAMELESS
SIGH
SMOKE
SNAG
SPREAD
STATESMAN
STEEP
SUEDE
SUET
SURFACE
SURREAL
TAKEN
TEENAGE
TITBIT
TOP
TRIBE
VOYAGE
YES

8

9

ABACUS
AIRWAVE
ALWAYS
AMPLE
ANACONDA
ANAEMIA
ART DECO
ASWOON
AUDIO
BAD
BAIL
BATH
BEGAN
BLOWFISH
BOAT
BRASS
BRISK
BRUTE
CATERER
CLARET
COBRA
DELIGHT
DENIM
DRAMA
DRESSER
ELEVEN
EVIL
FOLK-DANCE
GLASS
GLOBAL
HAYDN
INN
IRON
KEEPSAKE
KILLING
KIT
LEFT
LIST
LOLLY
LUGGAGE
MAID
NIECE
NINE
OUTDO
PEA
PLATO
PLUS
POLKA
PROMOTE
QUAFFED
RAVE
SAFFRON
SCAM
SCORPIO
SEPAL
SEQUINS
SHIRE
SNAFFLE
SOVIET
STOUT
STRAW
STRICT
SUGAR
SWEAR
SWEET
TEASPOON
TURF
TWEED
USED
VIOLA
VOICE
WIDEN

9

10

ACNE
AGLET
ALIGN
BEDDING
CAMEO
CARESS
CHAPS
COBBLER
CUPID
EEL
EFFECT
ELFIN
EMAIL
ESSAY
FLU
FURZE
FUSS
GODDESS
GOUDA
GRAN
GROW
ICEBERG
IMMUNE
INJECTS
INSIST
INSULIN
JADE
JOKE
JUSTICE
KIWI
KNIT
LAUGHTER
LESS
LLAMA
MAMMAL
MAST
MATTRESS
MODEM
NUDE
NULL
NUMERAL
OBSESS
ORPHAN
PERCENT
PHONE
PRETTIEST
RAISE
RATTAN
REPRODUCE
REVIEW
ROSE
SADIST
SAVINGS
SEAWEED
SKEWER
SORE
SOUR CREAM
STRATAGEM
STROP
SUM
TOG
TRANSIENT
TRIPE
TUTEES
USED
WEIRDNESS
WRAP

10

11

ABASE
ABOVE
ABSEIL
ACT
ADHESIVES
AGENCY
AMBLE
APEX
ARISE
ASSUAGE
AVENUE
BACTERIA
BAKER
BASIC
BICYCLE
BIPED
BLASPHEME
CAPE
CARETAKER
COFFEE
CRETE
CURATE
DUB
EASY
EFT
ELAN
ENJOY
EPIC
EQUINOX
EXAM
EXIT
GRIEF
HAZY
HECTIC
HEIR
IMAGE
INTRIGUE
IRONED
JOKE
LARVA
MAGIC
MARINA
MASONRY
NOVELTY
OBLIGE
OPERATIVE
RITUAL
RYE
SAGO
SCEPTRE
SEASIDE
SEDATED
SEEP
SHED
SNARE
SPINELESS
STERILE
SWAYED
THROAT
TORNADO
TREND
TRIBE
TRICKSTER
TURBINE
TUSK
WASH
ZINC

11

12

ACHE
ADORE
ALARM
ALMS
AMATEUR
AVARICE
AWRY
BEAST
BEEFY
CHASSIS
CHEESE
CHOLERA
CLAM
CRASS
CREDITOR
CUPID
DENIZEN
DUD
ENSNARE
EXHORT
EXORCISM
GREENS
GRIT
GYMNASTIC
HOMER
ISSUE
JACKDAW
JESTER
KHAKI
LARKS
LUKEWARM
MACBETH
MOHAIR
NEWS
ONUS
ORATE
OSCAR
OUNCE
PAN
PITCH
PLATEAU
PLY
RACKETS
RAGS
RAZOR
REACTOR
RECEIVE
RETINUE
SCENT
SCONE
SKIP
SLEIGHT
SOLAR
SPREE
SQUIB
STANCE
STEP
STERLING
SUEDE
SUMP
SURGE
SWAT
TEETH
TIE
TOES
TOGA
TORUS
TREAD
TUDOR
URGENT
VESPER
WHALE

12

13

ABETTOR
ABUT
ACRES
AGAPE
AGILE
ARENA
ARTIST
ASSAY
ATHLETE
BANQUETED
BARRIE
BASIL
BRAVADO
CERISE
CLAW
COTERIE
CREEK
EDITING
ELM
ENAMEL
GAVEL
HAVANA
HEARSE
IRATE
ISLE
IVY
JUMP
LARGESS
LAST
LYNX
MACE
MAGAZINE
MEDIATE
MORTAR
OFFA
OSTRACISM
PANDA
PICKAXE
PLAYTHING
PLIANT
PRECISE
PRO
QUAY
REACTOR
RESCUE
REVERE
SATELLITE
SCHNITZEL
SETT
SHALE
SHOEMAKER
SLALOM
SOUP
SPACE
SWAG
TEA
TENON
THIEF
TOLL
TRASH
TREFOIL
TWOTIMER
UNDIES
UNFED
VEIL
WING
ZINC

13

14

ADAMANT
AILMENT
AIRLINE
AMATEUR
ANTENNA
APTLY
ASP
ATLANTA
CACTI
CHUM
CROAKY
CROWBAR
DAISY
DROOP
EATEN
EON
EQUINOX
ERASER
EROSION
EXCLUDE
FLEET
GOAT
GRATUITY
HALCYON
HERO
HORATIO
HUSKY
HYENA
IDEA
IGUANA
INFORMAL
JAMBOREE
KENNEL
KHAKI
KIWI
LAMPREY
LARYNX
LATCH
LEEK
LITRE
LOG
MAYOR
NOMAD
NURSE
OMEGA
ONION
OSIER
PLAZA
POLAR
PRIM
REGAL
RELIC
RESETTLE
REVEL
RIDE
RITZ
ROARED
SAMBA
SATYR
SHED
SHREWD
SKETCH
STY
TALON
TIARA
TILE
TRADE
TRAPEZE
TRUE
UNIVERSAL
YARN
YEAR

14

15

ACRID
AGED
AISLE
AMERICA
AMPLE
ANTRE
AQUATIC
ARC
ARTICLE
ASKS
ATTIRE
BABOON
BADGE
BAIT
BEAD
BEEFY
BETA
BINGO
CAGE
CHAIR
CHARADE
CILIA
CINEMA
CLAM
COMATOSE
ELAN
ERNEST
EXACT
EXORCISM
FAWN
FLARE
FLOAT
GNAT
GRAFT
GRIDDLE
HERD
IMPLANT
JEALOUSY
KOALA
KRAFT
LARGE
LEASE
LEO
LIBERATE
MAGAZINE
NEAREST
NICOTINE
NUGGET
PACKING
PEACE
PERGOLA
REALISE
REFUGEE
SAFARI
SALVO
SHALE
SHIRE
SILENCE
SPAR
STATION
STOAT
TAPIOCA

15

16

ABACK
ABUT
ANEMONE
ANKLE
ARENA
ARTFUL
ARTISAN
ASPIRE
AWAKE
AWE
BABY GRAND
BAIL
BALE
BANE
BARBER
BARGE
BASE
BATHTUB
BATON
BEAK
BEMUSE
CABAL
CENTURY
CIDER
COMET
DESPAIR
DIET
EARN
ELK
FLUX
HAUNT
HEW
JESTER
JEWELLER
KIT BAG
LAIR
LAZY-BONES
LEASE
MACHETE
MARQUEE
MISFIT
MISTAKE
MUSLIN
NEWS
NIECE
OUTLET
OVERJOY
POLO
RECEDE
RIM
ROUGE
RUN OUT
SCAR
SCEPTRE
SERE
SEVENTEEN
SHAM
SKIMPY
SLACK
SONIC
SPATULA
UNITE
WAIL
WAREHOUSE
WARPLANE
WRISTBAND
XYLOPHONE

16

17

ADDER
ADDITION
ADOPT
AROMA
ASSET
ATTIC
BACKLOG
BANDAGE
BARRIER
BATTLE
BLEACH
BOATER
BOOT
BREAD
CADET
CANTER
CAVE
CHEF
CODE
COMET
CORRECT
COSY
CRATE
CREPE
DAREDEVIL
DAYTIME
EDGE
ELEGANT
ETNA
EXCEED
FALCON
FORCE
FORT
GAP
GOAT
HEW
IGLOO
INCOME
INSPECTOR
ITEM
LAPDOG
LARVA
LEOPARD
LIVESTOCK
LOTION
MOTORBIKE
PALM
PARISH
PAT
PEARL
PIGGYBANK
PLAY
POD
RECYCLE
REEF
REFECTORY
SAUCEPAN
SUSHI
SWAT
TAKEOFF
TERN
TIARA
TRAPEZE
TRENCH
TUTU
WILLOW
WRESTLE

17

18

ACONITE
ANISE
BATH
BEAM
BERGAMOT
BURDOCK
CARAWAY
CELERY
CHEF
CHIVE
COMFREY
CORIANDER
COTTON
CRESS
CUMIN
CUP
DILL
ELFIN
EMMY
EYEBRIGHT
FLAGEOLET
GOOSE FOOT
HYSSOP
KEPI
LAND
LETTUCE
LIME
MACE
MARE
MARTYR
MEAD
MINT
MOSAIC
MUSTARD
NEROLI
NOSEBAG
OCCUR
OREGANO
OSPREY
OXYGEN
OZONE
PANPIPES
PAPRIKA
PARSLEY
PAS
PICOT
PINT
PRIMROSES
RICER
SAGE
SAUCER
SCOPE
SEEDS
SENNA
SESAME
SIR
SPICE
TEAROOM
THYME
TONIC
USAGE
WAFT
WHEATMEAL
WOAD
YAM

18

19

ACCENT
ADVANCE
AGREE
ALIEN
ALOE
ALPHABET
APEX
ARNICA
BASSOON
BRAVE
CART
CAVIAR
CHEF
COMET
CORN
CRAYON
CURRANT
DECADE
DOVE
DUVET
EXTROVERT
FACTOR
GLASS
GRENADE
HEAT
HOUSE
INTO
KNEE
LADDER
LIQUOR
MANIFESTO
MASTER
MINT
MONEY
NEAT
NURSE
OLIVE
OPERA
OXFORD
PEAR
PERGOLA
PLINTH
PROGNOSIS
RADIATOR
RECYCLE
RED CARPET
REMOVAL
RIB
RIPE
SAFFRON
SAND
SATE
SAVE
SLEDGE
SPORTS CAR
SURNAME
TEXTILE
TIN
TITAN
TOKEN
TOMES
TRIBUNE
TWO
VIPER
WATERSHED
YAP
YIELD

19

20

ACID
AGRA
APOLLO
APOSTLE
ARCHWAY
AROMA
ARTISTE
ATHLETICS
BAKER
BALE
BILBERRY
CANTER
CHANT
COTTAGE
DANGEROUS
DRAMA
EBON
ECLECTIC
ENCAMP
ENTER
FACT
FRIENDS
GREENLAND
GUEST
INDIA
IRAN
LATIN
LATTICE
LAYOUT
LEANTO
LEO
LEVERET
LIFEBOAT
LUPIN
MANIFESTO
MESS
MOBILE
MOOSE
NOUGAT
ODDS
ODE
OMBRE
OVEN
PIGLET
PILOT
PROVERB
REBELLION
RIGHT
SHALLOT
SHINGLE
SHOULDER
SILK
SIMMER
SNAP
STARGAZER
STEAMER
STEEL
TAILOR
TAROT
TASK
TOAD
TREMOR
UNION
WARM
WRITHE

20

Codewords

Codewords are crosswords without conventional clues and with all the letters changed to numbers. There is method to this madness, as all the letters of the alphabet are assigned their own number between 1 and 26. These numbers change from one puzzle to the next.

You are given some clues, but they are fairly scant. You will see that in the solution grid two or three letters will have been solved for you. The rest is up to you and your vocabulary.

There are three parts to each puzzle: first there is the main grid, where numbers appear in the corners of the squares; second is the solution grid, where you can place each letter of the alphabet in its numbered box as a reference; third is an alphabet where you can check off the letters as you solve them. Every letter in the alphabet is used.

You may be familiar with similar puzzles to Codewords, but beware: the puzzles in this book contain proper nouns and some phrases. You may find place names, names of famous people and hyphenated words. While this adds slightly to the difficulty of the puzzle, it doubles its entertainment value.

1

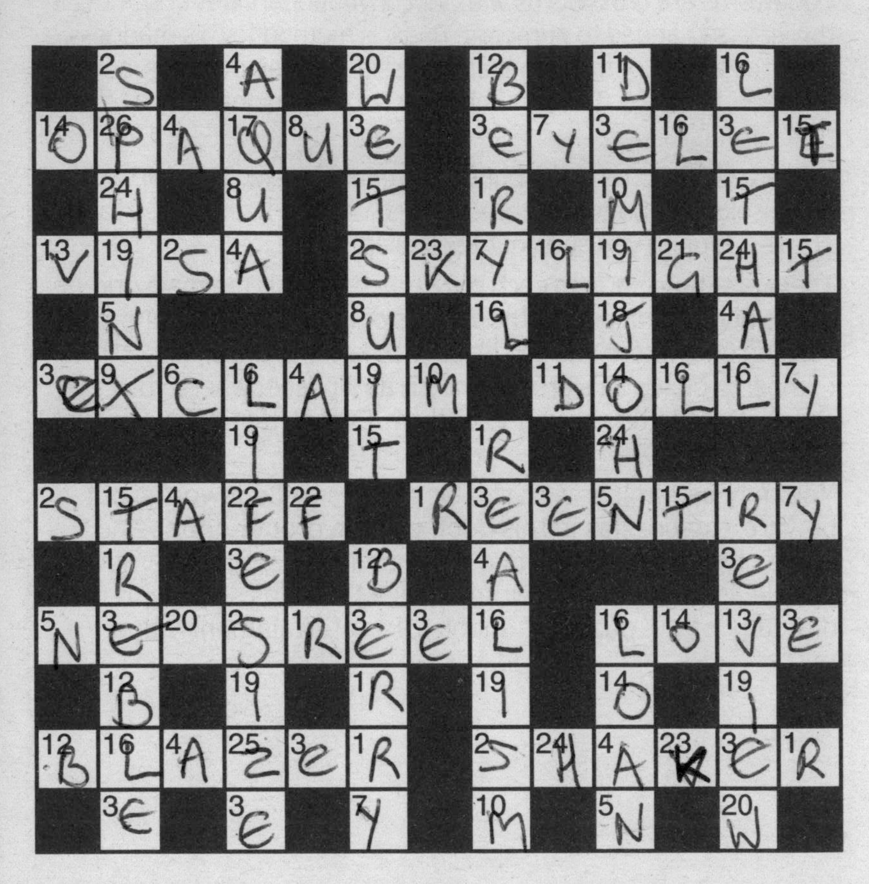

A B C D E F G H I J K L M N O P Q R S T U V W X Y Z

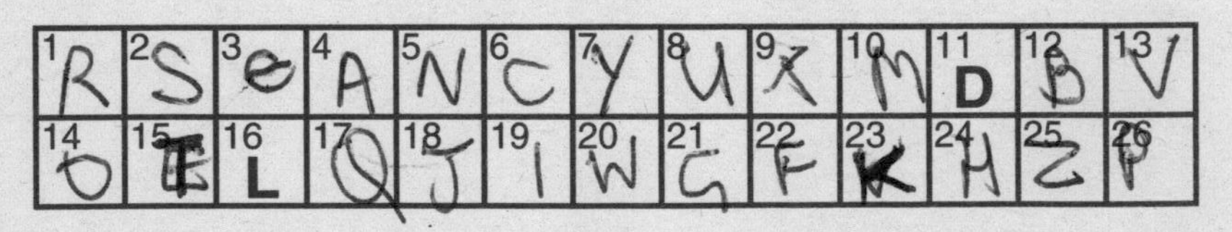

2

	22		3		21		26		23		12	
12	13	19	14	22	9		21	24	10	5	1	19
	26		9		10		4		8		22	
26	23	23	12		2	17	3	8	8	26	5	7
			5		2		24		17		20	
21	11	22	22	25	22	9		5	22	6	3	14
	26				5		7				17	
21	25	26	24	20		23	3	21	21	3	17	22
	24		26		22		17		10			
4	15	19	21	3	16	10	22		2	26	5	20
	18		3		10		23		11		12	
14	10	3	9	22	26		23	22	26	7	12	11
	17		12		17		26		19		18	

A B C D E F G H I J K L M N O P Q R S T U V W X Y Z

1	2	3	4	5	6	7	8	9	10	11	12	13

14	15	16	17	18	19	20	21	22	23	24	25	26
								E	M			

3

4	12	13	26	■	11	18	18	2	7	21	18	17
12	■	26	■	7	■	9	■	3	■	26	■	16
7	26	12	23	18	18	9	■	24	16	19	3	17
13	■	5	■	23	■	16	■	6	■	12	■	26
17	12	7	13	12	■	13	5	3	9	1	26	■
18	■	■	■	■	■	8	■	12	■	18	■	10
7	16	13	3	17	7	■	7	13	12	25	20	12
13	■	26	■	18	■	4	■	■	■	■	■	7
■	10	4	18	13	21	18	■	13	18	5	10	21
17	■	12	■	21	■	1	■	12	■	12	■	23
4	26	22	26	26	■	14	18	3	5	25	12	4
18	■	16	■	5	■	12	■	13	■	10	■	18
9	16	22	26	11	18	24	11	■	10	21	26	15

A B C D E F G H I J K L M N O P Q ~~R~~ S ~~T~~ U V W X Y Z

1	2	3	4	5	6	7	8	9	10	11	12	13
				R								T
14	**15**	**16**	**17**	**18**	**19**	**20**	**21**	**22**	**23**	**24**	**25**	**26**

4

15	19	26	5	14	16	24	■	22	26	17	9	13
19	■	24	■	1	■	14	■	16	■	26	■	2
20	11	9	13	20	7	16	20	24	■	22	26	15
22	■	■	■	24	■	17	■	8	■	19	■	21
20	5	22	20	3	■	20	11	17	24	20	5	20
■	■	19	■	16	■	8	■	■	■	25	■	10
20	10	26	5	20	19	■	20	8	9	26	4	20
11	■	9	■	■	■	8	■	26	■	24	■	■
4	21	23	20	19	20	17	■	17	24	20	8	8
19	■	12	■	26	■	16	■	8	■	■	■	9
26	15	26	■	21	10	18	19	16	20	10	6	26
21	■	9	■	24	■	18	■	5	■	16	■	19
10	26	23	20	3	■	2	20	26	24	10	20	3

A B C D E F ~~G~~ ~~H~~ I J K ~~L~~ M N O P Q R S T U V W X Y Z

1	2	3	4	5	6	7	8	9	10	11	12	13
												H

14	15	16	17	18	19	20	21	22	23	24	25	26
	G				L							

5

8	9	17	13		10	15	14	5	25	3	1	4
9		14		14		9		12		14		14
23	13	25	17	22	18	24		18	12	11	13	12
16		17		25		9		14		11		16
6	14	20	22	13		12	14	23	11	18	6	
14				1		20				19		25
1	23	25	9	15	17		3	14	19	16	15	13
15		7				22		12				14
	12	9	25	25	1	14		19	3	14	18	25
11		13		19		6		14		2		3
18	4	13	12	14		22	14	23	11	14	5	13
11		21		12		18		13		16		15
18	26	13	12	10	15	18	2		22	13	15	15

A B C D E F G H I J K L M N O P Q R S T U V W X Y Z

1	2	3	4	5	6	7	8	9	10	11	12	13
					M							
14	15	16	17	18	19	20	21	22	23	24	25	26
								B				

6

■	14	■	16	■	16	■	16	■	14	■	8	■
15	21	24	18	25	5	■	21	2	18	17	21	25
■	25	■	17	■	6	■	3	■	11	■	19	■
19	18	17	18	■	4	9	23	2	21	1	23	22
■	■	■	14	■	17	■	16	■	3	■	11	■
9	14	3	21	4	23	16	■	4	18	16	21	17
■	18	■	■	■	22	■	16	■	■	■	3	■
25	11	22	22	5	■	19	23	14	2	11	22	22
■	12	■	17	■	22	■	19	■	21	■	■	■
14	21	10	22	13	4	18	19	■	3	18	7	6
■	20	■	7	■	9	■	22	■	13	■	21	■
25	18	7	22	11	3	■	16	26	22	11	7	22
■	3	■	3	■	6	■	2	■	11	■	18	■

A B C D E F ~~G~~ H I J K ~~L~~ M N O P Q R S ~~T~~ U V W X Y Z

1	2	3	4	5	6	7	8	9	10	11	12	13
	T											

14	15	16	17	18	19	20	21	22	23	24	25	26
			L		G							

7

	24		25		7		4		25		1	
2	23	13	14	23	8		12	19	22	6	9	4
	11		1		18		23		23		8	
4	16	18	12		12	18	4	16	24	23	8	7
	19				22		1		20		18	
26	8	19	19	5	19	8		7	9	23	8	21
			6		16		25		24			
18	24	16	19	16		26	23	24	19	18	26	26
	17		11		24		8				8	
24	18	15	4	3	23	9	11		12	8	19	21
	8		18		12		18		19		11	
10	14	9	11	24	19		3	17	19	19	5	19
	4		13		8		22		20		21	

A B C D E F G H I J K L ~~M~~ N O P Q ~~R~~ S T U V W X Y Z

1	2	3	4	5	6	7	8	9	10	11	12	13
M							R					
14	**15**	**16**	**17**	**18**	**19**	**20**	**21**	**22**	**23**	**24**	**25**	**26**

8

6	21	16	2	26	16	12		20	16	24	14	14
26		24		8		15		15		25		26
17	26	4	21	11	18	24		26	1	5	24	16
14		10		18		21		20		14		12
24	14	24	23	19		4	15	19	22	21	23	24
				4		13				4		4
8	21	5	5	24	4		1	5	14	24	24	16
15		4				21		24				
26	2	24	16	21	19	2		16	26	23	24	1
1		10		12		2		9		26		12
1	26	19	16	12		3	21	18	4	16	24	13
19		24		24		21		19		19		14
1	24	7	24	4		17	26	16	2	26	9	24

A B C D E F G H I J K L M N O P Q R S T U V W X Y Z

1	2	3	4	5	6	7	8	9	10	11	12	13
											T	
14	15	16	17	18	19	20	21	22	23	24	25	26
							O					

9

9	6	5	17	23		25	17	23	23	26	20	7
6		17		20		6		19		20		6
4	20	10	18	11	20	5		7	6	19	20	23
17		6		16		20		12		1		23
25	20	10	5	13		10	17	11	5	20	7	
7				17		19				23		17
17	4	8	12	7	17		25	20	24	14	17	5
1		7				5		3				9
	11	6	24	5	20	7		17	4	8	5	19
25		21		20		12		7		12		23
20	23	12	17	10		15	7	20	22	22	23	17
11		2		2		23		2		22		10
14	17	19	10	6	5	17		17	3	20	21	17

A B C D E F G H I J K ~~L~~ M N O P Q ~~R~~ S T U V W X Y Z

1	2	3	4	5	6	7	8	9	10	11	12	13
						R						

14	15	16	17	18	19	20	21	22	23	24	25	26
									L			

10

7	23	25	17	■	19	18	24	11	11	25	12	14
23	■	18	■	19	■	3	■	22	■	19	■	5
5	6	24	19	5	26	24	■	5	4	16	18	10
12	■	12	■	22	■	26	■	18	■	1	■	16
10	3	21	22	16	■	16	12	10	18	16	16	■
25	■	■	■	18	■	11	■	■	■	18	■	10
10	24	2	3	5	10	■	13	23	12	14	8	23
21	■	25	■	■	■	10	■	12	■	■	■	14
■	14	4	25	26	16	18	■	4	25	22	1	24
14	■	4	■	25	■	24	■	24	■	25	■	8
24	18	1	25	10	■	20	5	19	13	26	5	15
4	■	24	■	10	■	5	■	13	■	14	■	5
8	24	9	3	24	23	12	26	■	1	16	5	18

A B C D E F ~~G~~ H I J K L M N O P Q R S ~~T~~ U V W X Y Z

1	2	3	4	5	6	7	8	9	10	11	12	13
									T			
14	**15**	**16**	**17**	**18**	**19**	**20**	**21**	**22**	**23**	**24**	**25**	**26**
G												

11

20	11	13	4	10	8	25		20	11	5	20	24
5		2		21		5		11		12		8
19	8	26	12	6	24	15		18	11	25	5	1
8		11		25		15		25		26		5
15	11	13	6	5		5	17	5	23	12	13	6
				19		13				16		11
24	8	5	26	8	25		20	5	25	15	11	13
5		13				3		19				
15	25	5	13	3	12	15		14	8	22	8	26
20		6		24		25		10		11		12
24	11	25	3	8		10	13	13	8	25	9	8
8		5		8		20		20		15		12
15	12	17	8	25		7	12	15	20	24	8	13

A B C D E F G ~~H~~ I J ~~K~~ L M N O P Q R ~~S~~ T U V W X Y Z

1	2	3	4	5	6	7	8	9	10	11	12	13
		S				K						
14	15	16	17	18	19	20	21	22	23	24	25	26
										H		

12

22	24	23	10	■	5	11	5	2	■	26	8	7
5	■	18	■	8	■	12	■	10	■	5	■	8
23	10	8	18	11	12	4	■	18	8	21	12	6
22	■	5	■	13	■	14	■	23	■	1	■	23
25	24	6	19	8	■	8	11	10	13	5	8	■
24	■	■	■	15	■	18	■	■	■	20	■	9
26	12	14	16	10	18	■	23	8	19	10	8	24
7	■	12	■	■	■	21	■	13	■	■	■	10
■	11	12	11	11	13	10	■	14	13	8	2	2
8	■	16	■	13	■	23	■	12	■	18	■	19
14	18	10	7	10	■	18	8	3	5	12	13	5
5	■	18	■	2	■	10	■	10	■	26	■	12
21	8	17	■	2	19	10	1	■	11	8	18	6

A ~~B~~ C D E F G H I J K L M N O P Q ~~R~~ S T U V W X ~~Y~~ Z

1	2	3	4	5	6	7	8	9	10	11	12	13
										B		
14	15	16	17	18	19	20	21	22	23	24	25	26
			Y	R								

13

	23		16		12		23		17		6	
15	9	10	20	18	23		2	12	16	25	2	5
	25		16		11		25		1		15	
17	23	11	23		24	2	11	6	26	14	16	22
	5				16		26		16		18	
4	2	10	19	3	25	23		14	9	4	23	11
			3		5		6		12			
20	2	3	7	23		8	16	18	14	3	23	25
	20		7		6		16				13	
17	25	23	23	5	3	6	5		20	18	9	23
	16		25		14		23		23		3	
8	2	11	3	25	23		25	23	18	2	11	23
	14		2		25		21		11		21	

A ~~B~~ C D E F G H I J K L M N O P Q R S ~~T~~ U V W X Y Z

1	2	3	4	5	6	7	8	9	10	11	12	13
										T		
14	15	16	17	18	19	20	21	22	23	24	25	26
						B						

14

■	12	■	7	■	15	■	13	■	23	■	10	■
9	20	15	2	5	24	■	14	18	13	21	11	5
■	21	■	11	■	18	■	20	■	19	■	26	■
4	15	3	3	■	8	18	21	25	6	11	11	22
■	■	■	23	■	20	■	11	■	11	■	2	■
11	7	7	13	2	5	3	■	20	19	13	15	5
■	13	■	■	■	12	■	19	■	■	■	5	■
13	16	19	13	6	■	19	13	13	5	21	11	10
■	10	■	2	■	23	■	16	■	18	■	■	■
7	21	15	4	1	15	23	25	■	23	13	4	17
■	13	■	12	■	21	■	18	■	25	■	21	■
15	14	18	15	2	17	■	5	2	11	8	13	2
■	11	■	26	■	16	■	11	■	5	■	22	■

A B C D E F G H I J K L M N O ~~P~~ Q R ~~S~~ T U V W X Y Z

1	2	3	4	5	6	7	8	9	10	11	12	13
		S	P									

14	15	16	17	18	19	20	21	22	23	24	25	26

15

9	19	17	18	10		5	23	6	7	19	3	10
18		18		3		25		3		3		26
13	12	25	24	22	14	4		23	3	16	12	10
2		15		18		20		20		12		3
14	10	10	26	10		18	3	20	23	19	14	
23						12		12		3		3
24	8	23	14	20	6		13	10	23	1	12	10
12		9		14		14						18
	6	9	12	19	2	10		6	18	1	23	14
23		25		21		6		2		12		25
13	12	19	15	21		2	8	23	7	25	19	6
12		3		12		18		12		13		19
10	11	15	14	10	7	10		9	14	10	6	6

~~A~~ B C D E F G H I J K L M N O P Q R ~~S~~ T U V W X Y Z

1	2	3	4	5	6	7	8	9	10	11	12	13
					S							
14	15	16	17	18	19	20	21	22	23	24	25	26
									A			

16

7	19	23	8	1	3	25		22	8	19	23	14
17		19		19		16		26		3		19
3	9	9	26	20	19	9		9	16	22	3	23
23		2		14		8		19		18		4
16	3	26	9	24		25	8	6	3	8	17	12
				19		12				22		19
24	26	23	19	24	26		1	26	12	5	8	13
26		16				3		10				
18	14	19	25	5	8	11		17	11	1	26	22
8		25		22		18		19		22		26
12	14	3	25	26		8	17	5	12	3	21	26
3		24		19		22		8		26		24
5	14	26	15	5		5	14	22	3	15	5	16

A ~~B~~ C D E F G H I ~~J~~ K L M N O P Q ~~R~~ S T U V W X Y Z

1	2	3	4	5	6	7	8	9	10	11	12	13
B						J						

14	15	16	17	18	19	20	21	22	23	24	25	26
								R				

17

23	4	24	26	17	2	16	■	8	25	21	10	17
13	■	25	■	1	■	4	■	25	■	17	■	26
19	22	9	20	5	17	2	■	23	2	25	18	17
13	■	2	■	24	■	16	■	13	■	21	■	11
2	13	21	17	13	■	24	9	11	11	17	16	■
7	■	■	■	9	■	17	■	■	■	11	■	10
17	9	10	22	16	12	■	25	23	25	21	9	25
2	■	2	■	■	■	4	■	25	■	■	■	2
■	25	9	2	20	25	11	■	14	22	2	4	10
25	■	18	■	25	■	9	■	23	■	25	■	13
15	25	18	18	12	■	3	4	25	24	9	6	12
25	■	24	■	8	■	4	■	21	■	14	■	24
2	22	12	20	17	■	17	1	17	10	17	16	17

A B ~~C~~ ~~D~~ E F G H I J K ~~L~~ M N O P Q R S T U V W X Y Z

1	2	3	4	5	6	7	8	9	10	11	12	13

14	15	16	17	18	19	20	21	22	23	24	25	26
							D		C	L		

18

	23		9		14		14		14		1	
23	8	22	8	4	7		26	18	25	19	3	5
	22		22		15		18		11		6	
6	8	3	22		24	18	25	16	2	19	23	25
			25		5		25		3		26	
25	15	21	5	3	21	6		8	6	23	18	7
	8				15		24				8	
9	18	8	14	14		17	8	22	22	8	9	7
	12		24		26		14		21			
10	3	23	3	22	8	6	5		21	1	18	8
	24		18		15		2		20		21	
15	8	18	3	6	25		18	25	8	14	21	6
	6		5		21		25		13		1	

A B C D E F G H I J K L M N O P Q R S T U V W X Y Z

1	2	3	4	5	6	7	8	9	10	11	12	13
14	15	16	17	18	19	20	21	22	23	24	25	26
								L	G			

19

■	7	■	1	■	5	■	6	■	8	■	2	■
3	12	15	23	8	14	■	2	14	1	4	14	2
■	26	■	15	■	4	■	18	■	24	■	25	■
12	26	14	4	■	4	18	10	18	24	18	25	21
■	14	■	■	■	15	■	21	■	7	■	1	■
14	24	14	25	1	9	16	■	22	1	20	14	2
■	■	■	18	■	25	■	7	■	2	■	■	■
22	14	24	24	21	■	22	1	23	20	24	18	25
■	24	■	13	■	14	■	25	■	■	■	4	■
19	15	7	22	1	22	5	14	■	23	18	4	14
■	10	■	1	■	18	■	9	■	8	■	17	■
11	15	18	24	15	9	■	16	14	1	6	18	16
■	2	■	24	■	21	■	1	■	6	■	22	■

A ~~B~~ C D E F G H I J K ~~L~~ M N O P Q R S T U V W X Y Z

1	2	3	4	5	6	7	8	9	10	11	12	13

14	15	16	17	18	19	20	21	22	23	24	25	26
								B		L		

20

26	14	7	1	8	15	12		4	3	21	7	26
12		23		22		26		19		23		8
21	23	18	20	18	3	5		10	23	19	6	24
10		6		11		18		10		16		17
12	6	7	19	15		20	23	12	5	16	12	15
				12				23		15		3
12	15	9		21	7	19	15	24		12	13	12
25		15		10				20				
1	15	12	6	12	22	5		18	23	17	19	5
3		25		7		19		8		15		11
26	2	3	19	17		12	15	12	13	7	5	12
12		23		15		3		23		21		12
26	3	12	21	12		20	7	24	6	12	22	5

A B C D E ~~F~~ G H I J K ~~L~~ M N O P Q R S ~~T~~ U V W X Y Z

1	2	3	4	5	6	7	8	9	10	11	12	13
				T				F				
14	15	16	17	18	19	20	21	22	23	24	25	26
	L											

Crosswords

1

Across

7 Hot spice (7,6)
8 Slaughterhouse (8)
9 Bold and impudent behaviour (4)
10 Run away (7)
12 Flat cap (5)
14 Small airship (5)
16 Extinct elephant (7)
19 Scowl (4)
20 Enormous (8)
22 Party game (7,6)

Down

1 Clothes (4)
2 Wobble (6)
3 Hampshire town (7)
4 Reject (5)
5 Climax of something (6)
6 Recklessly determined (8)
11 Conversation (8)
13 Mistaken belief (7)
15 Edge or border (6)
17 Grape variety (6)
18 Handle roughly (5)
21 Hairstyle (4)

2

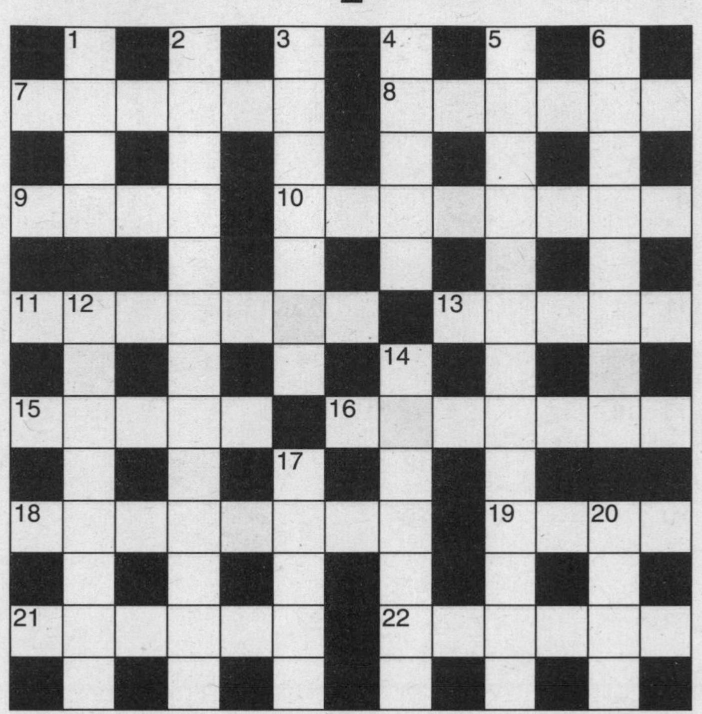

Across

7 Small travelling bag (6)
8 Dull grey (6)
9 Quick and skilful (4)
10 Fearless (8)
11 Smith who shoes horses (7)
13 Greek letter (5)
15 Prickly scrambling shrub (5)
16 Designate for a purpose (7)
18 Strong dislike (8)
19 Control or limit (4)
21 Afternoon rest (6)
22 Abandon or defer (6)

Down

1 Valley (4)
2 Military decoration (8,5)
3 Dress gaudily (7)
4 Sudden and concerted effort (5)
5 Make fun of (4,3,6)
6 Official list (8)
12 Goodbye (2,6)
14 Food decoration (7)
17 Essential (5)
20 Wander (4)

3

Across

7 Entertain with conversation (6)
8 English county town (6)
9 Ignoble (4)
10 Extreme and irreversible (8)
11 Hand over (7)
13 Enthusiastic (5)
15 Enjoyment or vigour (5)
17 Awkward situation (7)
20 Very unpleasant (8)
21 Rudely brief (4)
22 Rock salt (6)
23 Tray (6)

Down

1 Put air into (6)
2 Cabbage (4)
3 Small falcon (7)
4 Cheerful (5)
5 Pause (8)
6 Give an account of (6)
12 Fearless (8)
14 Varied (7)
16 Commotion (6)
18 Small amount (6)
19 Recipient of gift (5)
21 Carbonated drink (4)

4

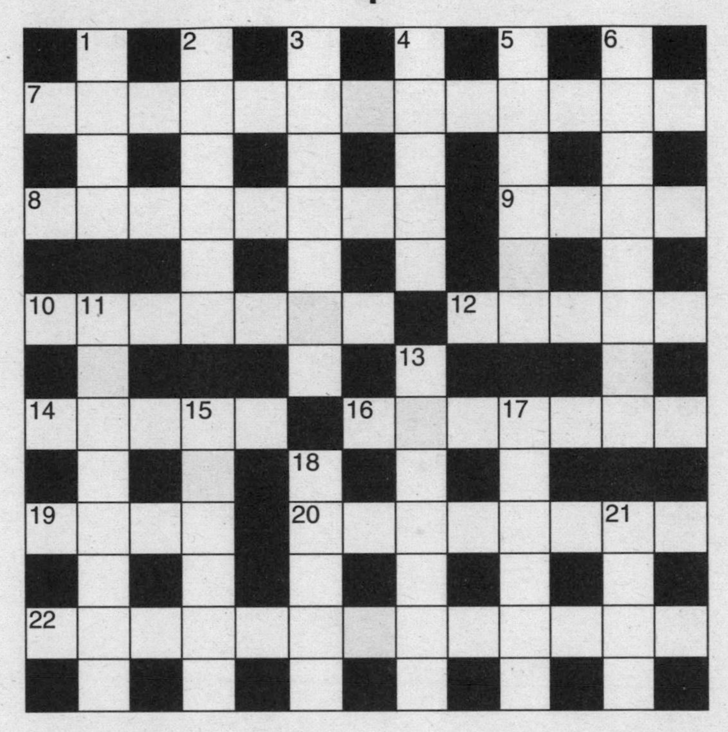

Across

7 Not carefully planned (3-10)
8 Cancel the punishment of (8)
9 Donkey cry (4)
10 Roman goddess of wisdom (7)
12 Preserved in sugar (5)
14 Love deeply (5)
16 Wailing female spirit (7)
19 Excessively abundant supply (4)
20 Divers breathing apparatus (8)
22 Not done on purpose (13)

Down

1 Floating sheet of ice (4)
2 Rare (6)
3 Deprive of courage (7)
4 French composer (5)
5 Burrowing rodent (6)
6 Political step or initiative (8)
11 Lazy (8)
13 Aptitude or talent (7)
15 Large and plump (6)
17 Yellowish complexion (6)
18 Auctioneer's hammer (5)
21 Indian leavened bread (4)

5

Across

- **7** Wide-brimmed hat (6)
- **8** Skillful (6)
- **9** Nutmeg spice (4)
- **10** In poor condition (8)
- **11** Children's construction set (7)
- **13** Soft and fluffy (5)
- **15** Mawkishly sentimental (5)
- **17** Edge of a road (7)
- **20** Eye disorder (8)
- **21** Primary subtractive colour (4)
- **22** Woman's undergarment (6)
- **23** Cause to become (6)

Down

- **1** Deceptive outward appearance (6)
- **2** Headland (4)
- **3** London district (4,3)
- **4** Large ray (5)
- **5** Very severe (8)
- **6** Dabbling duck (6)
- **12** Ornamental climbing plant (8)
- **14** Intense joy (7)
- **16** Public speaker (6)
- **18** Make insensitive (6)
- **19** Daryl Hall and John --- (5)
- **21** Nose (4)

6

Across

7 Country house (6)
8 Flowering shrub (6)
9 Incentive (4)
10 Absurd misrepresentation (8)
11 Capable of being drawn out (7)
13 Sticky semi-fluid matter (5)
15 Principle or belief (5)
16 Woman's sleeveless top (7)
18 Having high moral standards (8)
19 Quick and skilful (4)
21 Remove from office (6)
22 Mischievous child (6)

Down

1 Hairstyle (4)
2 Examination of one's own thoughts (13)
3 Largest city in Washington (7)
4 Tediously unoriginal (5)
5 Bowl-shaped aerial (13)
6 Naturally occurring sugar (8)
12 Cosmetic (8)
14 Hasty and not thorough (7)
17 Squalid dwelling (5)
20 Anti-aircraft fire (4)

7

Across

7 In abundance (6)
8 Not transparent (6)
9 Talk wildly (4)
10 A setting (8)
11 Vehicle shelter (7)
13 The underworld (5)
15 Small firework (5)
17 Modulation of voice (7)
20 The fashion industry (3,5)
21 Ballpoint pen (4)
22 Relating to spring (6)
23 Tricky question (6)

Down

1 Tropical fruit (6)
2 Habitual repetition (4)
3 Frenzied (7)
4 Asian peninsula (5)
5 Crustacean shell (8)
6 Pointless (6)
12 Spotless (8)
14 Artist's board (7)
16 Musical note (6)
18 Wading bird (6)
19 Heraldic black (5)
21 Carry (4)

8

Across

1 Quick look (4)
3 Card game (8)
9 Bitterness (7)
10 Outcome (5)
11 Daisy with large flowers (5)
12 Dessert apple (6)
14 Sailor's song (6)
16 Resembling bears (6)
19 Violin (6)
21 Paint solvent (5)
24 Go into (5)
25 Indian oven (7)
26 Ridiculously inadequate (8)
27 English river (4)

Down

1 Small-toothed whale (8)
2 Premium Bond selector (5)
4 Curt (6)
5 Dry and brittle (5)
6 Italian composer (7)
7 Excessively quaint (4)
8 Not openly displayed (6)
13 Pieces of mosaic (8)
15 Pilot (7)
17 Part of the eye (6)
18 Balance unsteadily (6)
20 Pub game (5)
22 Spacious (5)
23 Prolonged dispute (4)

9

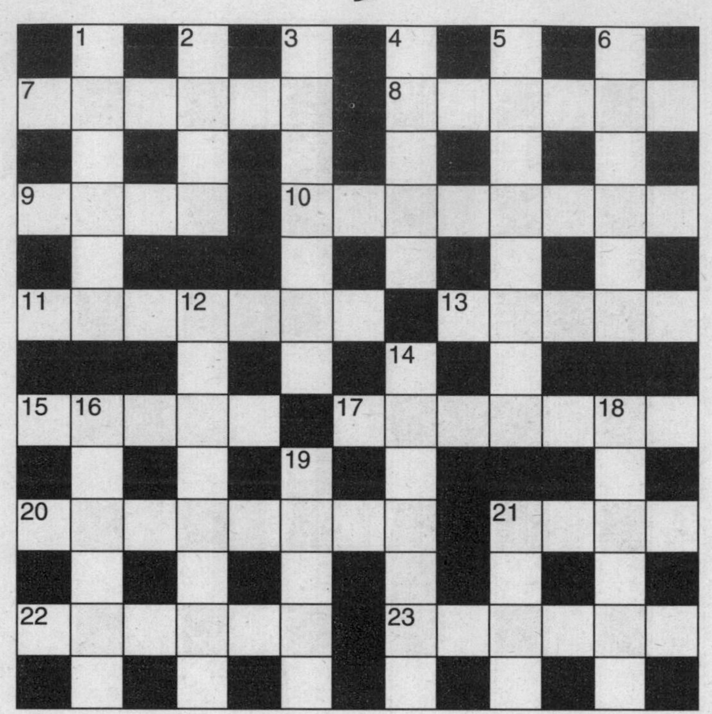

Across

7 Seasoned sausage (6)
8 Submit for inspection (6)
9 American university (4)
10 Precise and clear (8)
11 Decorate gaudily (7)
13 Molten rock (5)
15 Group of eight (5)
17 Move backwards (7)
20 Excessively flattering (8)
21 Capital of Norway (4)
22 Cushioned footstool (6)
23 Bay tree (6)

Down

1 Architectural front (6)
2 Central part of a church (4)
3 Pale lager (7)
4 Narrow waterway (5)
5 Form mental image of (8)
6 Light inert gas (6)
12 Recognise (8)
14 Very unpleasant (7)
16 American vulture (6)
18 Abdominal organ (6)
19 Breed of dog (5)
21 Reproductive cell (4)

10

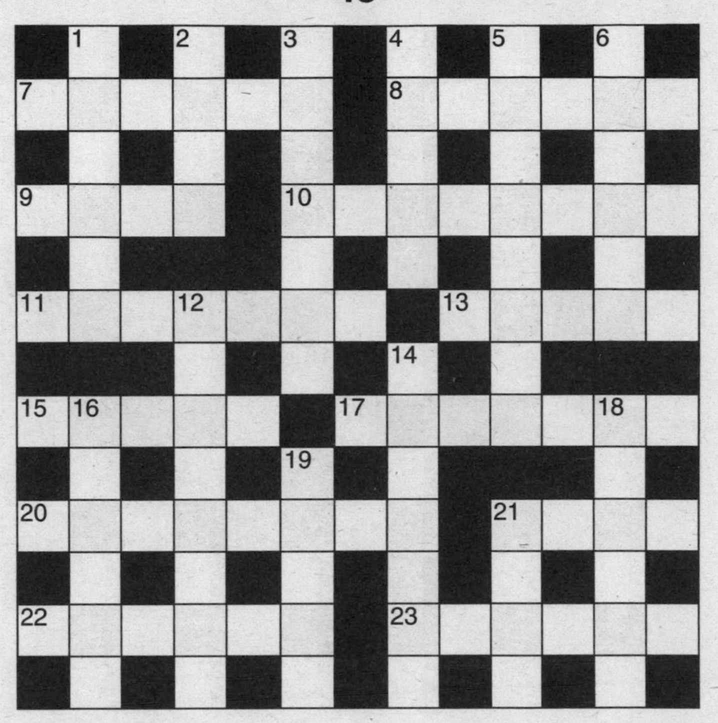

Across

7 Antiseptic solution (6)
8 Deceitful person (6)
9 Outburst of laughter (4)
10 Eucharistic offering (8)
11 Windpipe (7)
13 US silent film comedian (5)
15 North African mountain range (5)
17 Alter so as to mislead (7)
20 Freedom of action or expression (8)
21 Pole-driven boat (4)
22 Antenna (6)
23 Black eye (6)

Down

1 Empty or boastful talk (3,3)
2 Stretch of boggy ground (4)
3 Reduced in rank (7)
4 Pig food (5)
5 Captain Nemo's ship (8)
6 Serious crime (6)
12 Daddy-long-legs (5,3)
14 Food decoration (7)
16 Soup serving dish (6)
18 Guitar manufacturer (6)
19 Towelling fabric (5)
21 Bucket (4)

11

Across

1 Barrel-like container (4)
3 Branch of mathematics (8)
9 Soft leather (7)
10 Large stove (5)
11 Telltale (5)
12 Hand tool (6)
14 Unkind person (6)
16 Picturesque cave (6)
19 Expensive (6)
21 Edible crustacean (5)
24 Trivial complaint (5)
25 Prehistoric period (4,3)
26 Monocle (8)
27 Very small amount (4)

Down

1 Arrogantly confident (8)
2 Trap (5)
4 Evaluate (6)
5 Intriguing object (5)
6 Merciful (7)
7 Captain Hook's first mate (4)
8 Shellfish (6)
13 Gloomy (8)
15 Social insect (7)
17 Bird of prey (6)
18 Words of song (6)
20 Fish basket (5)
22 Flooded with water (5)
23 Man-eating giant (4)

12

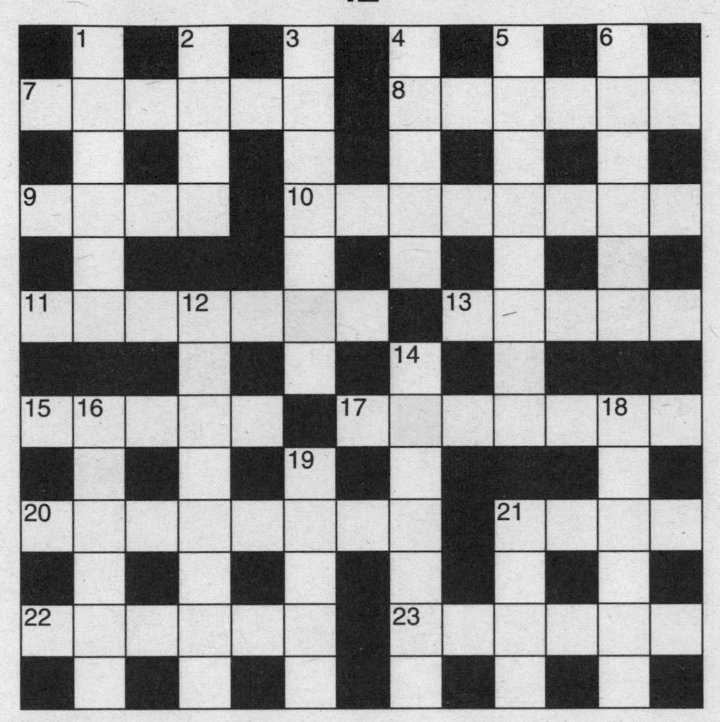

Across

7 Herb (6)
8 Lack of interest (6)
9 Benign skin growth (4)
10 Criticise harshly (8)
11 Italian composer (7)
13 Go for a swim (5)
15 Daughter of Zeus (5)
17 African republic (7)
20 Predict or estimate (8)
21 Wind instrument (4)
22 Having a good knowledge of (2,4)
23 Jacket (6)

Down

1 West Indies island (6)
2 pulled tight (4)
3 Refuse (7)
4 lucky (5)
5 Crustacean shell (8)
6 Roof-covering (6)
12 Thin and emaciated (8)
14 Make anxious (7)
16 Book of the OT (6)
18 Wading bird (6)
19 Rapid (5)
21 Frank and communicative (4)

13

Across

7 Horrifying (13)
8 Small turtle (8)
9 Long journey (4)
10 Salmon spear (7)
12 Icy cold (5)
14 Publicly denounce (5)
16 Hasty and not thorough (7)
19 South East Asian republic (4)
20 Relating to trees (8)
22 Anxiety or dismay (13)

Down

1 Delight (4)
2 Traditional English dance (6)
3 Thwart (7)
4 Companion (5)
5 Cheerfully indifferent (6)
6 Of low quality (8)
11 Lift (8)
13 Paraphernalia (7)
15 Struggle against (6)
17 Elf or fairy (6)
18 Bet (5)
21 Soon (4)

14

Across

1 Cut of beef (4)
3 Strong inclination (8)
9 Non-professional (7)
10 Cuban dance (5)
11 Male bee (5)
12 Chemical element Ag (6)
14 Ball game (6)
16 Chase after (6)
19 Assemble (6)
21 Master of ceremonies (5)
24 Scold (5)
25 Workshop (7)
26 C. 500 -1100 AD (4,4)
27 Chief of Roman gods (4)

Down

1 Done carelessly (8)
2 American state (5)
4 Way out (6)
5 Scallop roe (5)
6 Having no purpose (7)
7 Durable wood (4)
8 Admire deeply (6)
13 Practise (8)
15 Keyboard instrument (7)
17 Not level (6)
18 Suave and refined (6)
20 Dog-like mammal (5)
22 Cotton twill fabric (5)
23 Having a pH of less than seven (4)

15

Across

7 Electrical household device (6,7)
8 Of the highest quality (8)
9 Hang loosely (4)
10 Jump-jet (7)
12 Parody (5)
14 Italian city (5)
16 Wind instrument (7)
19 Liquid unit (4)
20 Harsh conditions (8)
22 UK Prime Minister (3,6,4)

Down

1 Fast-moving shark (4)
2 Landscape painter (6)
3 Indefinitely many (7)
4 Greek letter (5)
5 Heavy blow (6)
6 Prosperous (4-2-2)
11 From the beginning (2,6)
13 Defensive wall (7)
15 Clothing (6)
17 Angelic being (6)
18 Jewish leader (5)
21 Playing card with three spots (4)

16

Across

1 Cloying sentimentality (4)
3 Indian city (8)
9 Hard, silvery-white metal (7)
10 English poet (5)
11 Strict (5)
12 Considered (6)
14 Take in information (6)
16 Covering (6)
19 Gossip (6)
21 Private teacher (5)
24 Constellation (5)
25 Essential oil (3,4)
26 Spectator (8)
27 Unit of heredity (4)

Down

1 Person skilled in shooting (8)
2 Set of twenty (5)
4 Fleet of warships (6)
5 Nautical length of 200 yards (5)
6 Outpouring (7)
7 Skin condition (4)
8 Evening meal (6)
13 A person's buttocks (8)
15 Breed of dog (7)
17 Relating to the stars (6)
18 Spirit (6)
20 Circular painting (5)
22 Abrupt (5)
23 Company emblem (4)

17

Across

1 Warm and secure (4)
3 Governance (8)
9 Wondrous (7)
10 Fine net fabric (5)
11 Tuft of feathers (5)
12 Atomic number 8 (6)
14 Stamen part (6)
16 Equivocate (6)
19 Small earthquake (6)
21 Spurious (5)
24 In operation (5)
25 Catch in a trap (7)
26 Urgent request (8)
27 Badger's burrow (4)

Down

1 Dark grey (8)
2 Root vegetable (5)
4 US wildcat (6)
5 Sandwich (5)
6 Minor illness (7)
7 Search (4)
8 Soft shoe for a baby (6)
13 Outlook (8)
15 Exclude (4,3)
17 Surprise attack (6)
18 Pressing (6)
20 Unit of length (5)
22 Solemn (5)
23 Freshwater fish (4)

18

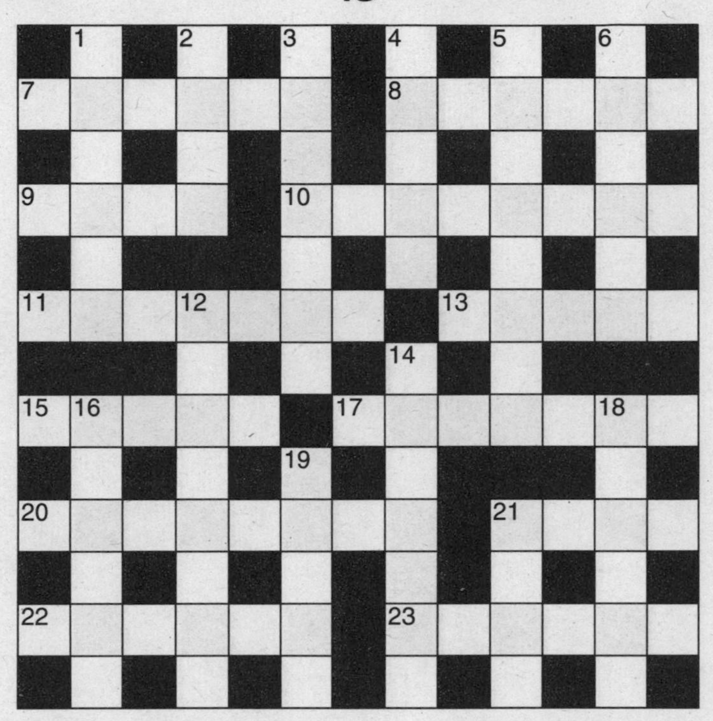

Across

7 Felt hat (6)
8 Sloping typeface (6)
9 Joke (4)
10 Holiness (8)
11 Bewilder (7)
13 Ornamental mat (5)
15 Palm leaf (5)
17 Kneeling cushion (7)
20 And so on (2,6)
21 Lout (4)
22 Higher in rank (6)
23 Discuss (6)

Down

1 Threat (6)
2 Skin blemish (4)
3 Wailing spirit (7)
4 Wicked person (5)
5 Inclined to dissension (8)
6 Flower part (6)
12 Disease outbreak (8)
14 Weighing apparatus (7)
16 On the contrary (6)
18 Barrel maker (6)
19 Tired (5)
21 Sharply curved (4)

19

Across

1 Male deer (4)
3 Definite and clear (8)
9 Outdo (7)
10 Lacking experience (5)
11 Harass persistently (5)
12 South American river (6)
14 Abandon (6)
16 Economize (6)
19 Blackcurrant liqueur (6)
21 Go over again (5)
24 Pool table covering (5)
25 Raise (7)
26 Excessive confidence (8)
27 Have faith in (4)

Down

1 Meddler (8)
2 Ribbed cotton trousers (5)
4 Grape variety (6)
5 Reddish-brown dye (5)
6 Capital city of Lybia (7)
7 Ship's company (4)
8 Chat (6)
13 Extreme anger (8)
15 Sports arena (7)
17 Part of the eye (6)
18 A particular view (6)
20 Contemptuous smile (5)
22 Stop (5)
23 Border on (4)

20

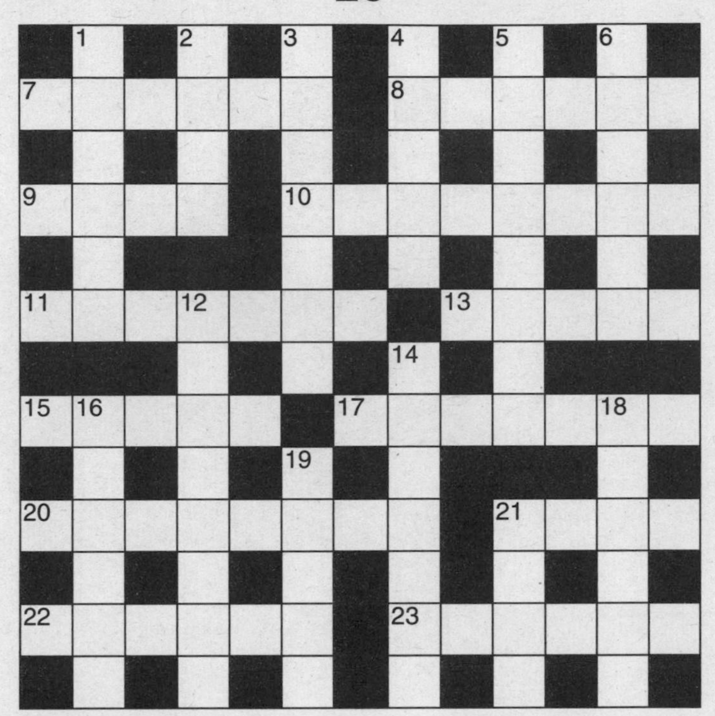

Across

7 Ancient Roman council (6)
8 Clever (6)
9 Engrossed (4)
10 Hurry (4,2,2)
11 Butlin's entertainer (7)
13 Horse (5)
15 Fossilized resin (5)
17 Modulation of voice (7)
20 Preliminary test (5,3)
21 Roll up neatly (4)
22 Plum-like fruit (6)
23 American tap (6)

Down

1 Calm (6)
2 Deliberately taunt (4)
3 Sackcloth (7)
4 Father (5)
5 Wood preservative (8)
6 Relating to apes (6)
12 Deep crack in a glacier (8)
14 Enlarge (7)
16 Innumerable (6)
18 Wading bird (6)
19 Salt water (5)
21 Continuous change (4)

Pathfinder

Beginning with the letter in the upper left-hand corner, follow a continuous path to find a list of words relating to the puzzle heading. The trail passes through each and every letter once, and may twist up, down or sideways, but never diagonally.

1. CAKES AND PASTRIES

C	U	P	C	I	N	N	I	R	A	K	E	W	E	L
J	E	C	U	N	E	A	W	L	B	C	E	G	D	L
A	K	A	A	T	L	M	S	H	C	A	V	I	U	T
M	E	B	E	E	L	O	N	M	I	K	E	C	F	A
T	T	R	T	A	O	K	A	A	W	D	N	T	T	R
A	A	O	A	C	T	L	B	C	A	T	A	O	L	E
R	L	W	G	A	S	A	A	A	B	H	S	R	E	I
T	O	N	T	K	A	V	B	R	N	B	A	I	D	N
B	C	I	S	E	C	R	A	O	O	U	C	H	A	E
A	O	E	E	F	K	E	B	A	E	N	A	E	M	P
T	H	B	R	L	C	A	M	C	R	T	S	R	E	E
T	C	L	O	A	A	M	U	L	T	P	N	T	T	T
E	G	A	F	P	J	P	R	E	R	A	I	O	R	I
N	R	C	K	C	S	U	E	T	A	R	K	R	U	T
B	U	E	N	O	F	F	H	C	O	I	R	B	O	F

2. ATTENBOROUGH FILMS

B	I	R	G	E	N	T	L	E	M	E	L	I	T	T
R	K	K	F	R	G	E	L	G	N	N	O	O	E	L
I	N	T	O	E	E	N	I	R	A	T	D	N	I	L
G	U	H	E	A	H	C	S	Y	E	H	R	L	N	A
H	D	E	U	T	T	E	D	O	C	T	O	Y	E	R
T	W	L	G	E	A	P	E	O	N	E	R	W	H	F
O	A	E	A	S	C	I	S	N	E	W	E	H	T	A
N	L	D	L	I	H	C	S	E	R	E	H	E	D	N
R	N	R	F	A	C	P	A	J	Z	A	T	N	E	D
O	I	E	O	R	Y	A	R	U	I	B	F	R	E	O
C	S	N	O	G	A	R	K	E	L	E	Y	A	H	M
K	R	A	T	A	W	A	R	E	H	T	R	D	S	C
B	E	B	E	N	L	I	U	S	T	H	C	O	N	H
R	H	R	G	D	A	C	R	L	I	N	E	W	I	A
O	T	I	D	H	I	H	O	S	D	N	A	L	L	P

3. BREEDS OF DOG

B	U	L	L	D	O	G	H	U	S	K	Y	S	P	A
U	H	S	R	E	X	O	B	I	L	C	E	L	G	N
A	I	H	A	T	I	A	E	E	L	O	U	N	A	I
H	H	E	M	E	H	N	S	B	Y	H	O	D	E	E
U	C	E	L	R	P	D	I	I	E	L	L	J	B	L
A	G	P	A	D	E	O	R	C	R	L	E	A	R	P
D	O	D	D	P	H	B	F	H	G	U	S	C	E	I
A	U	N	D	O	S	E	N	O	R	R	S	K	H	N
C	H	E	L	O	N	R	C	H	E	C	U	R	C	S
H	S	R	I	D	A	M	S	N	Z	H	L	A	O	N
D	E	R	E	L	M	A	N	A	U	E	D	N	L	P
S	E	T	W	E	R	E	G	E	N	R	N	D	L	E
R	E	T	T	R	P	P	N	W	F	O	U	P	I	K
M	T	I	T	O	I	E	A	A	R	O	P	A	P	I
A	S	F	F	W	H	T	I	N	E	M	E	S	E	N

4. WORKS OF SHAKESPEARE

A S Y K E I T T H E M E R C H
S U O I M M D I M A E C I N A
A N U L E U S S D R E A M E N
N E V E R G H T B A O D M V T
D A S N N I O N O A N A U F O
A E U I L E T T U O D H C O L
D M R E W B H O M E J O R I A
O S E R A M I R E L U C I K N
N I F H L Y N G O C L T N R U
A E O S L C E L P D I E G A S
S M R E S E N A A N A Y L S J
U A M H W T D T T R A N E E U
R T I T E A S S T N T O A A L
E E N F L H W R E I H T R C I
T H G O L T E L L W E N A S U

5. COOKING UTENSILS

W	A	F	F	L	O	A	R	D	R	E	G	G	R	T
E	M	R	I	E	B	S	S	S	E	R	E	T	O	A
T	O	O	I	N	G	P	E	T	M	P	M	I	M	R
E	M	N	P	R	E	E	R	E	A	E	A	N	D	B
R	R	C	P	M	P	P	P	C	I	S	E	A	M	A
R	E	H	O	I	U	L	A	B	L	T	L	R	N	I
O	H	A	E	L	T	K	D	R	R	A	G	I	E	S
L	T	T	M	L	A	N	A	E	A	N	T	E	L	K
L	W	O	O	D	P	I	F	R	P	W	H	I	L	I
I	N	G	N	E	S	F	E	Y	G	E	H	S	T	E
N	I	S	O	N	R	E	N	I	N	E	C	K	A	R
G	P	M	T	S	E	R	I	A	R	S	E	G	R	T
I	X	I	N	P	D	C	D	E	T	E	N	O	N	I
N	O	W	O	O	N	O	N	R	S	R	E	P	I	N
G	B	L	B	L	E	L	A	M	A	N	D	O	L	E

6. LONDON UNDERGROUND STOPS

E	T	I	S	E	L	L	O	X	F	O	R	D	C	I
A	S	N	S	R	A	S	T	S	E	W	S	U	C	R
E	L	D	U	E	U	Q	E	T	T	E	D	O	T	O
D	B	I	R	H	T	R	E	M	S	R	G	N	N	W
O	M	A	Y	A	S	O	T	I	N	P	N	A	O	N
N	I	W	E	M	R	N	G	N	I	A	I	C	T	R
B	N	D	S	P	E	P	U	T	D	D	R	R	E	O
E	O	E	T	S	K	G	A	N	B	R	R	H	H	T
R	M	A	D	B	A	E	T	E	Y	I	A	I	E	B
N	R	O	M	T	X	U	T	O	C	D	F	T	H	A
I	S	C	E	N	B	R	G	E	S	G	E	O	W	N
N	E	E	C	Y	E	I	D	W	S	S	D	O	S	K
G	R	N	C	O	L	B	M	E	I	W	A	N	N	S
T	C	T	L	C	O	S	T	E	R	S	C	A	H	T
O	N	R	A	K	F	F	R	A	H	W	Y	R	O	J

7. NAUTICAL TERMS

A	R	F	R	D	E	G	U	N	S	C	A	Y	S	A
N	O	A	A	B	S	H	C	T	A	L	T	S	E	I
C	H	T	O	R	A	P	E	L	W	E	S	C	L	L
M	O	H	B	I	H	O	E	L	G	W	N	U	C	D
B	E	N	R	D	C	R	K	E	O	L	E	P	A	E
U	K	A	A	G	E	T	K	A	D	I	Z	P	N	C
L	A	B	T	N	I	H	C	G	E	N	Z	E	N	K
K	T	A	S	E	L	A	O	U	E	M	I	R	I	H
H	D	C	K	B	W	M	M	O	H	L	A	S	B	A
E	A	A	W	R	O	B	M	U	L	L	G	P	D	N
D	R	I	S	I	S	H	R	S	E	E	T	R	T	E
S	A	N	X	D	D	I	A	E	E	Y	N	E	N	R
P	W	L	O	G	I	P	D	Y	H	W	E	V	E	T
I	E	E	C	E	M	M	R	A	I	P	L	L	A	O
N	N	A	K	E	R	A	N	S	K	P	E	R	G	P

8. SPACE AND ASTRONOMY

M	A	R	S	A	O	I	S	H	A	L	C	O	M	E
N	A	T	I	S	R	D	E	E	P	L	S	S	P	T
V	M	O	T	T	E	J	R	H	O	E	Y	E	I	E
E	S	O	O	I	P	U	E	U	C	T	S	P	L	C
N	U	N	L	T	T	O	C	B	S	A	E	E	B	I
O	E	M	L	E	U	A	L	B	E	T	C	R	R	T
R	T	E	O	R	L	X	A	L	L	I	A	I	O	A
N	E	P	P	A	P	Y	G	E	E	O	P	H	N	L
T	U	T	U	N	E	O	U	D	T	N	S	E	O	G
B	A	N	O	S	A	O	O	G	A	N	Y	L	I	R
L	O	N	R	T	K	R	L	U	O	Y	T	I	V	A
A	C	S	L	L	I	T	C	S	H	M	A	T	R	A
C	E	T	E	A	N	T	U	T	E	E	S	U	U	N
K	L	O	I	T	U	L	P	O	L	D	E	R	N	U
H	O	N	N	E	B	A	S	N	T	T	U	H	S	S

9. MUSICAL INSTRUMENTS

G	R	O	A	S	S	O	O	N	F	L	U	T	E	D
U	A	B	B	N	I	R	A	O	O	D	I	R	E	I
I	T	O	E	A	H	I	C	O	O	L	O	C	G	D
R	U	H	P	P	W	S	T	L	C	E	L	L	A	R
D	U	R	R	A	N	C	O	E	C	F	G	U	B	I
Y	G	D	A	N	I	E	J	P	I	R	E	N	E	N
D	N	Y	H	P	T	L	N	A	B	A	C	C	N	E
O	A	M	S	I	S	L	P	I	E	L	I	H	O	T
L	O	S	S	P	E	O	S	N	A	T	N	H	B	S
I	N	I	A	B	E	D	N	G	I	R	O	O	M	A
N	A	T	N	C	L	O	E	L	Y	N	M	R	O	X
P	I	A	I	Y	B	U	K	E	S	T	R	N	R	O
M	U	R	L	M	L	O	C	R	E	H	A	T	T	P
P	R	T	O	B	G	E	N	C	Z	E	H	U	E	H
E	T	V	I	A	L	T	R	O	I	S	A	B	N	O

10. COCKTAILS

H A R V E Y W A N C K R U S S
A B L O O T A B G A R E A X I
C S L C M A L L E L S D N E A
A N I P O E A M R B N B A L N
R S M O L T R M A N O W L A S
D O A Y I D T I N A G N L Y A
I C L O T E I N H T A I S D N
T R E R A C I D A T P O O N G
E E A R N R S N N I O L D A R
Q M M I S E E A G L R B Y R I
U M E K C V X L M S E E M B A
I A R H R I O S O M U L A G G
L L I C E R N I S W C E R N I
A S C A W D T G C O A D Y I N
O N A E B E H N O L R I S L S

11. LARGEST ISLANDS

G	O	R	N	E	O	M	R	B	A	F	F	I	S	L
R	B	N	A	D	N	A	A	O	T	N	O	N	I	A
E	A	D	L	S	A	D	C	R	C	S	H	A	R	N
E	E	J	S	O	L	A	S	I	I	H	R	E	T	D
N	N	A	I	U	S	G	A	A	V	U	G	A	A	S
L	I	V	H	T	I	E	R	I	N	I	A	T	M	U
A	U	A	A	N	O	N	E	S	L	A	T	B	A	N
N	G	N	L	D	Z	N	M	S	E	N	I	R	L	D
D	W	O	S	L	U	E	I	O	L	D	S	I	S	S
N	E	R	I	C	D	W	N	L	L	E	K	A	K	R
I	D	T	H	U	N	F	A	A	B	A	N	T	N	I
R	N	A	L	B	A	O	P	S	N	L	S	A	A	L
E	H	O	E	A	L	U	S	A	I	A	I	S	N	I
L	D	K	C	I	D	N	I	K	L	N	N	M	A	A
A	N	K	A	I	D	O	H	H	A	D	O	V	E	D

12. PERIODIC TABLE

H	R	O	R	B	O	N	N	E	M	A	M	I	U	M
Y	D	G	A	R	I	N	E	O	M	G	U	N	I	S
H	N	E	C	O	E	I	N	N	U	N	L	U	R	I
E	R	O	N	N	S	T	I	S	I	E	A	S	O	L
L	O	C	I	C	E	R	R	O	D	S	M	C	H	I
I	B	K	N	O	N	O	O	D	N	I	U	H	P	C
U	M	E	T	B	A	G	U	I	A	C	S	L	S	O
M	U	L	L	A	G	E	L	U	I	T	M	O	O	N
L	I	C	E	N	N	N	F	M	T	A	U	R	H	P
I	L	O	S	I	A	O	N	U	I	N	I	I	A	R
T	L	P	R	C	M	X	E	M	D	I	C	N	E	G
H	Y	P	A	B	M	Y	G	C	A	U	L	I	S	O
I	R	E	C	R	U	I	M	H	N	M	A	U	S	N
U	E	R	N	O	N	E	O	R	A	V	C	M	A	P
M	B	Z	I	M	I	K	R	Y	P	T	O	N	T	O

13. ECONOMIC TERMS

C	O	M	M	I	S	S	I	O	I	N	A	T	N	A
Y	C	N	E	N	I	U	R	N	E	V	N	I	O	L
R	D	D	V	S	R	P	K	B	T	E	T	P	T	D
E	E	E	L	O	A	T	N	A	A	S	E	E	B	E
V	K	V	U	A	E	C	Y	B	R	T	S	N	F	U
E	N	A	L	T	Y	A	R	A	E	M	S	S	N	N
N	I	U	D	I	L	T	E	S	G	E	A	I	O	D
U	L	N	E	O	A	E	H	A	N	N	D	E	G	B
E	X	D	R	N	C	F	C	N	O	T	I	T	D	U
I	E	A	I	N	S	I	X	S	I	L	U	T	M	M
N	D	N	T	C	A	X	E	T	N	I	Q	R	O	O
D	N	O	B	O	T	M	U	O	U	E	D	A	C	D
U	W	R	M	M	E	P	L	C	R	O	K	E	R	I
N	R	I	U	I	M	P	S	K	B	O	H	A	H	T
D	E	T	E	R	E	R	R	E	D	L	E	R	S	Y

14. COLOURS

P	U	M	P	K	I	N	I	M	E	M	E	R	A	L
U	B	U	R	C	E	M	N	C	K	H	E	S	R	D
R	U	M	R	C	E	A	E	E	N	A	R	A	E	C
N	T	B	E	A	V	U	D	L	I	R	I	P	B	E
R	E	B	O	R	O	P	R	A	P	L	H	P	M	R
M	V	A	C	D	C	P	E	D	T	E	J	O	A	I
I	T	L	L	I	T	I	N	O	O	Q	A	W	E	S
L	O	T	A	N	S	N	E	N	H	U	V	H	M	A
I	C	A	T	H	Y	D	T	P	N	I	A	I	A	R
O	I	M	E	O	G	I	T	I	N	K	N	T	U	I
N	R	K	E	B	M	O	A	O	R	A	S	E	Q	N
L	P	H	Z	R	A	U	B	N	F	F	N	O	A	E
I	A	A	N	O	T	N	T	B	G	U	O	C	E	P
N	I	K	G	E	N	M	I	U	R	N	M	H	R	E
E	N	M	A	N	O	S	R	C	Y	D	M	I	S	R

15. WELL-KNOW CHEFS

R C S O P H I A R Y R I N M A

A N R E V I E G S E H E I P R

Y A D C A L G D R D O T E O C

M L E O R O R Y I C K S R D O

O B L I L E I O P O I R R R N

N D I N U I G L H T S H E O R

Y N A O C M S F E N O C W G A

W O S T C A O H L L V N H E M

O H M N I J N T I L E A I T S

R T I A O K E I P E I E J Y A

R N T N R F F A R L T N G S T

A A H O E Y K J U E H I E E A

L M P S M O E R U H M T T B L

L O G U H H N L E D A T O S L

T H H F E A R N Y W H I N R M

16. COUNTRIES OF THE WORLD

D	Y	A	F	R	L	A	Y	S	E	T	N	A	M	J
E	B	Q	A	A	A	U	C	I	I	L	A	U	T	A
N	I	J	R	N	M	A	E	A	V	B	D	N	A	P
M	L	A	I	C	E	D	A	I	N	A	N	I	I	A
A	D	M	D	N	A	O	I	N	R	D	A	S	D	N
R	N	A	I	B	L	R	F	L	O	A	L	I	N	I
K	A	I	M	I	E	E	G	A	J	N	O	A	I	N
T	L	C	A	A	C	R	D	N	Y	K	P	A	T	A
U	I	A	N	P	I	M	R	S	E	E	E	R	N	U
R	A	R	E	A	N	A	E	K	U	N	L	G	E	R
K	H	U	C	K	E	N	J	R	A	Y	I	H	C	U
E	T	S	E	I	M	Y	M	A	D	I	W	A	Y	G
Y	I	S	E	S	E	Y	U	I	L	V	R	Y	A	U
H	T	I	R	T	B	E	I	N	A	E	O	S	D	E
A	I	A	G	A	N	L	G	E	M	S	N	W	E	N

17. AIRCRAFT

H O N M I L I N E R H U N T E
O O H G C R B M O B E D R O R
T L T I R I E L I D E R B C C
A L D L O A R G I L E P I N O
I A O B U G T I N A I P P U R
R B O E N O T M H C R E L H R
S P D L E R H S A S B Z A D I
E M I L B D A E P R U R N O C
A E B E R T R L A E S E E R A
P R O T M E R U C S M T H M N
L I E S O J I C H S E P E I E
A F I A N P E R E G L O L N J
N T N C O M R E S N E C I T U
E I G N P U J H E I A R J E M
S P L A L A N E A K T E J O B

18. CARTOON CHARACTERS

B	U	O	N	R	L	B	R	O	W	N	S	N	N	E
S	G	T	E	A	I	E	Y	T	A	D	Y	O	N	R
B	T	S	C	H	T	P	B	T	F	F	P	O	U	D
U	N	I	N	P	O	O	O	E	B	Y	C	O	R	O
N	I	E	N	C	M	I	E	P	K	D	E	Y	D	N
N	L	T	I	A	T	C	S	O	C	U	E	O	A	A
Y	F	H	W	O	O	K	U	P	W	I	L	T	O	L
H	D	E	L	I	D	E	O	E	E	W	Y	E	R	D
O	E	P	E	X	Y	Y	M	Y	S	O	D	O	O	D
M	R	O	F	T	B	O	O	E	U	O	D	P	W	U
E	F	O	H	H	I	B	C	S	O	D	N	E	K	C
R	N	L	Y	E	G	E	T	Y	M	J	A	C	R	P
S	O	V	S	C	O	A	H	O	O	E	M	K	E	O
I	S	E	T	A	Y	R	G	F	G	R	O	I	P	R
M	P	S	T	E	R	M	I	Y	Y	R	T	G	Y	K

19. AMERICAN STATES

A	S	K	A	T	I	Z	O	N	A	N	E	V	A	C
L	A	I	N	E	R	N	I	M	O	Y	W	A	D	O
N	A	A	R	X	A	G	N	N	E	S	O	D	A	L
A	I	M	O	A	O	O	I	A	W	O	T	A	R	O
M	S	O	F	S	C	R	M	S	I	R	U	K	S	A
I	I	N	I	C	I	E	H	H	G	T	O	A	N	S
S	U	T	L	A	X	G	A	I	N	O	S	S	I	N
S	O	A	W	M	E	O	T	I	M	N	G	I	M	E
I	L	N	E	N	A	N	U	C	A	G	R	A	A	B
S	K	A	N	E	M	K	R	H	D	E	O	F	M	R
S	R	O	Y	W	A	A	A	I	I	R	O	L	O	A
I	I	P	E	N	B	N	N	G	L	I	N	O	H	S
P	P	N	A	N	A	S	I	A	L	W	A	I	A	K
I	H	I	V	S	L	A	S	N	I	I	W	S	L	A
O	O	A	L	Y	A	S	N	O	C	S	O	I	K	O

20. WELL-KNOWN QUOTES

B	L	O	O	D	I	S	T	H	I	C	K	E	H	A
S	E	H	T	N	A	E	R	E	R	E	H	R	T	N
W	E	A	R	E	H	I	O	F	N	C	T	K	N	W
O	W	M	A	N	T	A	M	I	A	E	W	E	I	A
R	D	U	T	O	R	E	I	G	R	I	O	R	H	T
R	E	S	A	W	E	E	T	N	O	S	P	O	T	E
C	V	E	D	S	I	K	H	G	I	B	S	N	I	R
E	E	N	L	A	T	I	I	N	M	L	I	E	L	O
A	T	H	L	L	G	M	E	P	S	I	E	S	L	W
S	S	E	I	O	N	D	N	O	I	S	G	W	A	D
E	I	O	W	S	R	E	O	L	N	S	D	O	N	O
R	N	P	H	E	P	E	W	I	E	K	E	T	S	E
E	O	I	T	E	E	O	S	T	P	N	L	M	E	S
L	I	U	F	U	L	P	C	I	E	O	W	A	K	U
I	G	M	O	R	E	K	A	!	H	T	R	E	M	M

Wordsearch

Using the given list, try to locate all the words in the grid. Words can be found horizontally, vertically, diagonally and in any direction.

1. EQUESTRIAN TERMS

L B I U C P Y E A R L I N G H A C K I N G

C H E S T N U T H S R E H T I W D Z B A O

Q B T D L A B W E K S L S S T I R R U P F

R O S E T T E A X V D I T T M Z I V A C O

E L A G N I T R A M T V C A A D J K I H N

R F K P U R K M L U B E A E L B M D W O I

D Y X F A M K B D D C R N E D U L Z O O M

P V A I F C M L J B A Y T C Z P D E R F O

O R L R O C A O Y E R G E L P P A D R P L

G E X L P B S O E X R M R M I T S R A I A

R R T J E S H D G O O A N T H Y N E B C P

H E A I H A Y N E T T J C O S L A S L K O

F T P Z Y A I L R B S H O A T L F S E D L

I U R L I T K K F D F F D D Z I F A E G L

S S A I N N Q W E O O D D A H F L G H Y A

J G U E G F G D R I L O G K A P E E W M G

E Z V P N I D K L E O H Z K N E U H R K U

G E L S E R O M A K C A H G M R I R Y H M

G N I C A R C F C H A F F I U N L T S A M

C U R R Y C O M B R O W B A N D Q Z R N A

N Y O O G N I D L E G Z V Y T V J E V A B

BRIDLE
BROWBAND
CANTER
CARROTS
CHAFF
CHESTNUT
CURRY COMB
DAPPLE GREY
DRESSAGE
EVENTING
FETLOCK
FILLY
FLY SPRAY
GALLOP
GELDING
GIRTH
GRAZING
GYMKHANA
HACKAMORE
HACKING
HAYNET
HAYLAGE
HOOFOIL
HOOFPICK
JODHPURS
LIVERY
MARE
MARTINGALE
NUMNAH
PALOMINO
PIEBALD
PITCHFORK
RACING
ROSETTE
SADDLE
SKEWBALD
SNAFFLE
STABLE
STIRRUP
TRAILER
WARMBLOOD
WHEELBARROW
WHINNY
WITHERS
YEARLING

2. COUNTRIES

A Q Q C X J P C E I C N A T S I K A P S M
Q B F P V L A I B I M A N E C U A D O R K
B U L G A R I A W M E L L R A N D O R R A
Y U G O S L A V I A M A M A U R I T I U S
A G N O T R A T A Q W F Y T I A W U K A E
N E C V X Q U E P U O L E D A U G E M L Y
M A R U K R A I N E M Y M Y N N N A A Z C
L O D O M I N I C A W E E R N Y H P Y A H
Y E D R V M B C N M P K N E A A E L N L E
S C D G O U P T T U R A W A B N I A I T L
T N E R N J E P A U Q Z J L W T D E E G L
D A N U E I Y P T S E W X E H A C A K R E
N R A S V G K U N A M O Q U G H D C W E S
A F T S E V I D L A M C A Z T A E A O E Y
L U S I V R A A E G U N Q E D O N A T N R
N N H A E G N D E T I S N N X D M I U L A
I Z K L L D D R N A I S J E A M A B N A G
F M A C I A M A J A T N P V Z P R M I N N
H N Z D U A W E V E G V U E C V K A S D U
D B A W N S M G I Y A U G A R A P Z I S H
S U K Y K B A N G L A D E S H U S Z A N R

ANDORRA
BAHAMAS
BANGLADESH
BULGARIA
CANADA
DENMARK
DOMINICA
ECUADOR
EGYPT
FINLAND
FRANCE
GERMANY
GREENLAND
GUADELOUPE
HUNGARY
IRELAND
JAMAICA
JAPAN
JORDAN
KAZAKHSTAN
KENYA
KUWAIT
LIECHTENSTEIN
LITHUANIA
MALDIVES
MAURITIUS
NAMIBIA
NEPAL
NEW ZEALAND
OMAN
PAKISTAN
PARAGUAY
PERU
QATAR
RUSSIA
RWANDA
SEYCHELLES
TONGA
TUNISIA
TURKEY
UGANDA
UKRAINE
UNITED KINGDOM
VENEZUELA
VIETNAM
WALES
YEMEN
YUGOSLAVIA
ZAMBIA

3. ITEMS OF CLOTHING

T T T W C F K V R B D D I J Q J P A F X J
I S E H N S J R A B S T N H Y S A G N A T
U T L F L D U A V O X H I S A R W O N J K
S H G R E U F S C T W O K R C Y R T U F C
P G N D E R V K P K H N I C I A A M L K O
M I I Z R V S P A E E G B T D C P B X A R
U T S C P E O L G Q N T U P R E O U A F F
J L H P E Q S L I F L D T O R I E A L T Y
C Z O N F X C S L E Z A E P N L H X T A T
T X R Q V T X I E U B L V R T D A S N N R
I S T D O I L G T A P E W N S S A U I P U
U A S G V Q I K R Z S N A S V R K E K G N
S S W H N L I D I T J M A Z I E I W R P K
K G A X G L C F K T G R F C T P M C E D S
C N R E T A E W S A O D I E B M O L J N L
A I N P W U W T Y N A N L Z M O N F Q O L
R G N N W M N K G K U B A T H R O B E R A
T G P T Q U O P R T U J Q J Y Q W N B E R
J E R S E Y Z U V O C W X W U F D E O L E
B L O U S E B G D P D U N G A R E E S O V
V Z G S C A R F G N I K C O T S Y D O B O

ABAYA
BATHROBE
BIKINI
BLOUSE
BODYSTOCKING
BOLERO
BURKA
COAT
DOUBLET
DREADNOUGHT
DRESS
DUNGAREES
FROCK
GILET
JACKET
JERKIN
JERSEY

JUMPER
JUMPSUIT
KAFTAN
KILT
KIMONO
LEGGINGS
MANTLE
NEGLIGEE
OVERALLS
PULLOVER
ROMPERS
SARI
SARONG
SCAPULAR
SCARF
SHIRT
SHORTS

SINGLET
SKIRT
SOCKS
SUSPENDERS
SWEATER
TABARD
TANGA
TANKTOP
THONG
TIGHTS
TOGA
TRACKSUIT
TRUNKS
TUNIC
VEST
WRAP

4. COUNTIES

G C C C W A R W I C K S H I R E S S E X N

N V O O R K N E Y V A M Y I C T V H P Z L

U T A R I E M T J R N E N A H G A N O M W

O P S N K Q I U J Q F F O N W K M M V V E

E D N W O D R N A E F I M B L L M Z Z X X

D N A A D P T J R M T F P O Y G A W H L F

N A V L G Z N M I K L O F R O N A G Z Q O

A L A L E R A D L I K F L G G T A W W I R

L T C U G N D O S E U E V L E M N N K H D

R U F Q A L N N R S I Y E R R U S U G N A

E R N G E G F I A T F S F A Y O R K N A Y

H T H S F X H U R L E O D U B L I N A I O

T P E O C S K I D Y R L A G E N O D I H W

U X R L E Z M U B D A O H D X O T R H T I

S D A H D O R S E T T F M B E Q G S T O C

A R C B O H W J J U I H H T S N C I O L K

E S M U A I O K H T A E M T S E A M L T L

N Z C M F L L E T Y R O N E U E X K D S O

B O Y A M C R R N B E Z P B S O W E I E W

N J P O P E A R K C I R E M I L L N M W Y

G D E V O N C Y R O S C O M M O N T J T P

ANGLESEY
ANGUS
ANTRIM
ARMAGH
CARLOW
CAVAN
CHESHIRE
CLARE
CORK
CORNWALL
DEVON
DONEGAL
DORSET
DOWN
DUBLIN
DURHAM
ESSEX
FERMANAGH
FIFE
GALWAY
KENT
KERRY
KILDARE
LEITRIM
LIMERICK
LONGFORD
LOUTH
MAYO
MEATH
MIDDLESEX
MIDLOTHIAN
MONAGHAN
NORFOLK
ORKNEY
ROSCOMMON
RUTLAND
SLIGO
SUFFOLK
SURREY
SUSSEX
SUTHERLAND
TYRONE
WARWICKSHIRE
WATERFORD
WESTLOTHIAN
WESTMORLAND
WEXFORD
WICKLOW
YORK

5. LORD OF THE RINGS CHARACTERS

```
G A M L I N G F R O D O B A G G I N S W G
N D D R U D A M R O D T H E R A N G E R H
E E H U R I N T H E T A L L K U P G L I E
N N D W K I Z M H I G U T H L A F I R H Q
O E P O A G L O R F I N D E L G G G Q I N
B T K H E L F H E L M C K U A S O V S A I
H H T A X H C E L E B O R N A N X D T W U
C O D L O F T S E W F O D L O B M I R G L
E R N E O W Y N A T Q A O S W J Q O R R R
E I A E N A D V N U L G A G N O L R O F I
B I R H R E L O C F R R D N O R L E T O H
X X B F I W O V X P U O V L F C C T S K A
L O N Z H H G Z M M C G N B P X N H E A L
A G E Q O A N R A T S N E V E N E W R A B
V O K L R M I N Z Z R Z I M V R R A E N A
O M R N L A Z L N I F U R E D I G W K A R
R H E A E A F M M U L L O G H O W I J D A
D T H Z V V D O R E M O E N R F N D L R D
N O F G I M R A H I L Y I N F A R A M I R
A G R U R O B G N A Q U I C K B E A M C R
L V E L B M U R W O D I W D E R V O R I N
```

ANGBOR
ARAGORN II
ARWEN EVENSTAR
BEECHBONE
BERGIL
BOROMIR
CELEBORN
CEORL
CIRDAN
DAMROD THE RANGER
DENETHOR II
DERUFIN
DERVORIN
DUINHIR
ELFHELM
ELLADAN
ELROHIR
ELROND
EOMER
EOTHAIN
EOWYN
ERESTOR
ERKENBRAND
FARAMIR
FORLONG
FRODO BAGGINS
GAMLING
GANDALF
GLORFINDEL
GOLASGIL
GOLLUM
GOTHMOG
GRIMBOLD OF WESTFOLD
GUTHLAF
GWAIHIR
HALBARAD
HAMA
HIRGON
HIRLUIN
HURIN THE TALL
IMRAHIL
INGOLD
IORETH
LANDROVAL
NAZGUL
QUICKBEAM
SARUMAN
SAURON
THEODEN
WIDOW RUMBLE

6. BIRDS

N	R	A	J	T	H	G	I	N	J	E	K	E	I	B	O	L	H	T	I	D
I	D	K	C	O	C	A	E	P	T	N	F	H	A	W	F	I	N	C	H	A
B	D	V	B	A	W	N	T	I	T	E	U	L	B	C	N	I	I	J	H	I
O	F	B	B	L	A	C	K	B	I	R	D	L	Y	Q	U	A	I	L	A	C
R	Y	K	I	T	T	I	W	A	K	E	E	H	C	C	E	C	N	A	W	S
N	I	K	S	I	S	W	M	C	W	R	S	T	C	L	A	V	K	J	K	N
K	I	Y	Z	K	O	O	R	U	T	C	G	O	R	O	J	T	O	O	K	S
G	I	T	E	X	S	O	H	S	P	A	R	R	O	W	P	N	C	D	O	Z
B	O	N	R	L	W	T	E	M	A	C	S	U	S	G	U	R	J	H	X	E
U	M	L	G	A	L	K	A	M	H	T	T	D	S	H	F	E	A	M	E	B
L	I	P	D	F	M	O	C	R	A	S	Y	A	B	N	F	T	Q	F	K	R
L	J	U	R	F	I	E	W	U	L	G	K	Q	I	O	I	A	X	H	F	A
F	C	X	H	H	I	S	S	H	D	I	P	Y	L	C	N	U	C	V	S	F
I	I	M	H	Z	P	N	H	U	A	K	N	I	L	L	P	N	U	T	W	I
N	O	E	G	I	P	H	C	E	O	M	V	G	E	A	I	H	H	E	A	N
C	Q	E	I	Z	M	J	E	H	R	H	M	R	E	F	R	R	E	Y	L	C
H	C	H	I	F	F	C	H	A	F	F	U	E	N	J	U	K	F	R	L	H
W	L	I	A	T	G	A	W	R	S	T	O	E	R	S	N	E	R	W	O	Q
G	O	L	D	C	R	E	S	T	L	A	E	P	H	I	F	E	Y	J	W	N
G	R	E	A	T	T	I	T	U	U	R	N	C	H	A	F	F	I	N	C	H
K	C	O	N	N	U	D	V	R	G	T	H	T	H	L	A	P	W	I	N	G

BLACKBIRD
BLUE TIT
BULLFINCH
CHAFFINCH
CHIFFCHAFF
CROSSBILL
CROW
CUCKOO
DOVE
DUCK
DUNNOCK
FALCON
FLYCATCHER
GOLDCREST
GOLDFINCH
GOOSE
GREAT TIT
GREENFINCH
HAWFINCH
HAWK
HERON
HOBBY
HOUSE MARTIN
KESTREL
KINGFISHER
KITE
KITTIWAKE
LAPWING
MAGPIE
NIGHTJAR
PEACOCK
PHEASANT
PIGEON
PUFFIN
QUAIL
ROBIN
ROOK
SISKIN
SKYLARK
SPARROW
STARLING
SWALLOW
SWAN
TERN
THRUSH
VULTURE
WAGTAIL
WREN
YELLOWHAMMER
ZEBRA FINCH

7. HERBS & SPICES

F H I S L O A Y W E H A D I T E O F A S A

E G E B O P N R E G N I G C I N N A M O N

N E D T A R R A G O N N T A M A R I N D M

U M F C B A R M G B G U D A K I R P A P K

G T O M A G R E B E Y R L E F A I S S A C

R U B A Y T U S L A R E E F E F L U R K O

E N O K L E N O R B N O A D T S A I T H M

E O R F E J E R C N B K H O N N Y O P Y F

K A A M A N O N E E P T Z S E A I P C S R

P N G O V W O F R P L A M L E M I M P S E

R G E M E Z Y R C A P E R S I V Y R E O Y

N E R A S Q R M F I M E R S J V O H O P P

K L N D H Y O A W F R U P Y L S R L T C H

M I A R B N C R M Q A E S I S E E E C A L

G C A A C I I J A Q O S M T L E Y V H L K

A A S C N M H O P C M J X R A L E K I C D

R I V W S U C R U V A S L D U R I D V H H

L A L A H C V A K U C K F E J T D H C S C

I E G A V O L M H U E C I P S L L A C O N

C E H T Z A N I S E L A Y O R Y N N E P T

C A Y E N N E P E P P E R C A R A W A Y H

ALLSPICE
ANGELICA
ANISE
ASAFOETIDA
BASIL
BAY LEAVES
BERGAMOT
BORAGE
CAPERS
CARAWAY
CARDAMOM
CASSIA
CAYENNE PEPPER
CELERY SEED
CHERVIL
CHICORY
CHILLI PEPPER
CHIVES
CINNAMON
CLOVES
COMFREY
CORIANDER
CUMIN
DILL
FENNEL
FENUGREEK
GARLIC
GINGER
HYSSOP
KAFFIR
LOVAGE
MACE
MARJORAM
MINT
MUSTARD
NUTMEG
OREGANO
PAPRIKA
PARSLEY
PENNYROYAL
POPPY SEED
ROSEMARY
SAFFRON
SAGE
SORREL
TAMARIND
TARRAGON
THYME
TURMERIC
YARROW

8. FAMOUS BATTLES

S T I R L I N G B R I D G E V L L S D S X
N I E M A L A L E P M E H N R A E O X T L
N O T N E R T R A F A L G A R M I M Q O K
W X H R Z G X X F O C C I I E G H M E N S
K K I T A E K S O M A L A I I D I E J I N
D C O D A H D C L W T S K Z B M M B N R U
A T Q B A R N E T K C N P L P W T O R A D
R A W D G T A U P V A I G L B A N R O V R
G L U C C P D M R R E I R I R T I O H A E
N Y Q S U I A L C L K S B H I E A D G N V
I R B A T R T E W Q U G L E T R S I I P I
L A F E G E I N A J R N E G A L W N B V T
A C G A S L R I A W B I N D I O X O E C O
T Q W I L A N L G L O T H E N O F G L D R
S Y B I N K N K I S T S E C D T J K T Y I
J E K L E C I O Z T Y A I C L O Q D T U A
Z S S R K P O R I K Z H M Y Z F L F I Y F
M S M E U B R U K P D O O W U A E L L E B
U A O C R T B G R U B S Y T T E G L U B L
N L Z T S P M B D T E W K E S B U R Y C G
F P W B K Z Y B U N K E R H I L L O W B K

AGINCOURT
ALAMO
ARNHEM
ATLANTIC
AUSTERLITZ
BARNET
BELLEAU WOOD
BLENHEIM
BORODINO
BRITAIN
BULGE
BUNKER HILL
CULLODEN
EDGEHILL
EL ALAMEIN
FALKIRK
GETTYSBURG
HASTINGS
INKERMAN
KILLIECRANKIE
KURSK
LEIPZIG
LITTLE BIGHORN
MARATHON
NASEBY
NAVARINO
PLASSEY
SAINT MIHIEL
SOMME
STALINGRAD
STIRLING BRIDGE
TEWKESBURY
TOBRUK
TRAFALGAR
TRENTON
VERDUN
VITORIA
WAGRAM
WATERLOO
YPRES

9. FAMOUS AUTHORS

J J N F Z G N O R M A N B R I D W E L L Q
A I O R G E J O H N C R E A S E Y V H C G
M N L F U R Z Q W Q R L N H E S W A A O W
E W O X I A P V S R S N O P N A X N D R R
S I G I M R J R S S K I T N A B Z H D L E
M L E J G D A E U R O T Y A C F I U L C T
I L N K F D N C E L O R L E N S D N A Q H
C I N R V E E I S E C A B L R P L T O K G
H A A O G V T R R W N M D C R G H E R D U
E M C W I I D E D I I M I M Y E E R W A A
N S D L L L A N Y S B N N R R A X N U I L
E H C I B L I N S C O N E I F O V M A F S
R A R N E I L A K A R A N A W R I L P Z G
T K E G R E E Y K R L E O T O L S T O Y K
K E X E T R Y A Q R C S C S R T P R J C N
A S S Z P S Q D H O R A T I O A L G E R A
R P T Y A A H O O L E A C L A S K K U A R
L E O Y T Y L K P L Z B E A T Z V B N R F
M A U Q T D S D P R J N E I K L O T R R J
A R T G E O M B G N I K N E H P E T S B O
Y E S A N M D N O D L E H S Y E N D I S B

ALISTAIR MCLEAN
ANN M MARTIN
ANNE GOLON
ANNE RICE
C S LEWIS
CATHERINE COOKSON
CLIVE CUSSLER
DR SEUSS
ENID BLYTON
EVAN HUNTER
FRANK G SLAUGHTER
GERARD DE VILLIERS
GILBERT PATTEN
HORATIO ALGER
J R R TOLKIEN
J K ROWLING
JAMES MICHENER
JANET DAILEY
JOHN CREASEY
KARL MAY
LEO TOLSTOY
LEWIS CARROLL
NORMAN BRIDWELL
R L STINE
REX STOUT
ROALD DAHL
ROBIN COOK
SIDNEY SHELDON
STEPHEN KING
WILLIAM SHAKESPEARE
ZANE GREY

10. ART MOVEMENTS

```
N L K N B Z T I E D S M D I G W F L R P A
A N Q T I O A N I U I W M T A V D V U E R
R E T R A K L O F N Q S A I R B B R T U E
T O V I G W O L I E I O F F I Q I A U Q N
D I A B P I E M O V K E R F C S T R E S A
E S Y C J S A Z U A I C B A M D R E X E I
C M O U N L H A S H U P V R B E A Y P B S
O U L A I P F O A T W W B G I W T M R A S
P A B S T R A C T A R T N I M P E S E R A
S I M I H C M W T R A E V I A N E I S A N
S D D D S S E S T U C K I S M F R R S H C
Z Z R T I M S I R E T T E L X E T E I M E
M X Q L Y A M S I V I T C U R T S N O C S
S T A R L S T R A C I M E D A C A N N W T
I E N L O O H C S N O Z I B R A B A I M P
R E Q K N M O D E R N I S M A J C M S N O
U X E L D A R T N O U V E A U U J I M P P
T A F A H D P L U R A L I S M O H M H E A
U Q D A S H C A N S C H O O L P F A J Y R
F A M S I V I T I M I R P G R L H B U K T
I M P R E S S I O N I S M O N H L L F S P
```

ABSTRACT ART
ACADEMIC ART
ARABESQUE
ART DECO
ART NOUVEAU
ASHCAN SCHOOL
BARBIZON SCHOOL
BAROQUE
BAUHAUS
CONSTRUCTIVISM
CUBISM
DADA
EXPRESSIONISM
FAUVISM
FOLK ART
FUTURISM
GRAFFITI
IMPRESSIONISM
LES NABIS
LETTERISM
MANNERISM
MINIMALISM
MODERNISM
NAIVE ART
NEOISM
ORPHISM
PLURALISM
POP ART
PRIMITIVISM
PURISM
REALISM
RENAISSANCE
STREET ART
STUCKISM

11. BOTANICAL TERMS

Y T G E R M I N A T I O N C O R M F B E P

R N C Q L U S D I I C J L O Q Z L T A D E

R T W X H Y J E Z G H Q H N R O L N R A T

E J R T P E T X E V L Q E E R E E A K L A

B B H E U B V S F D O E D E G C K J T B L

F C I I E B T V R O R J T U T L N C H E K

C Z Z T U S E A T G O T M A P C N B U Y X

O H O L M J W R R C P E R B O L A P E S E

R A M R E S C E U I L A B U L B G R A F T

O M E S T P V E N Q A F O R L A S Z B E R

L P Y E L E R V K B S A F R E A T Z C A S

L H M W P H G A R P T E Z G N M O C A K O

A I R G A W N E C K U L A F B O L E N I P

A T P Q L Q H X R T A V E A N T O K O E C

T R L I U V B D M I E O O D N S N X P B I

T O I I F L S G N U G N U N O T F O Y B N

C P X U T T E N D R I L W A X N H U N U T

U O A L Y S E X M F G E N T W H S E J R V

P U T O O R I O D K E G W E K N D J R H W

X S M I E B G P B D A X W R D G V V B S V

W M S P L R E H K Z N D B I U X C K C I I

ADNATE
AMPHITROPOUS
ANTHER
AXIL
BARK
BERRY
BLADE
BOLE
BRACT
BULB
BURR
CANOPY
CARPEL
CHLOROPLAST
CONE
CORM
COROLLA
EVERGREEN
FLORET
FRUIT
GERMINATION
GRAFT
HERB
LATEX
LEAF
LEGUME
LOBE
NECTAR
NODE
NUT
PERENNIAL
PETAL
PISTIL
POLLEN
RHIZOME
ROOT
SEED
SEPAL
SHRUB
STEM
STOLON
STOMA
STYLE
SUCKER
SWARD
TENDRIL
TREE
TRUNK
TUBER
WEED

12. BEST SELLING ALBUMS

Z E F C O D L E D Z E P P E L I N I V W D
Z L L E H F O T U O T A B B A G O L D S S
P R I V A T E D A N C E R D L U F S F X H
Y H U V Y J A G G E D L I T T L E P I L L
S T V T D V Y F L F R V T S J D N I Q R Z
A I E V E I L E B T A H M D U A C C T E D
C A J K T Y G W M D E R B A K O E E R L R
O F T U V N A U A J A O V O D R S W U L A
M J D U A V S D O N L D Q N A Y K O E I U
E U J O X I D S I Y M U I W G E M R B R G
O R N Y C A H S R U O M U R N B E L L H Y
N R O B G U R T I H R Q L A I B T D U T D
O E O A A E S N D E X G O X C A A B E T O
V X N T H E N U V B A C K I N B L A C K B
E I R T P E Q E O W T S V O A V L Q K C E
R E O A L S N M R R Y V X E D D I Y I O H
E R T L L A W E H T E S X S Y Z C N H S T
B Q I Q K E W Y X V X G F J T Q A I R N M
D M B L T R U S Q I Y K N Y R T U P W S A
S A S W Q G L Q Y W V J W A I N O T S O B
D R L R F Y B X Y R O E H T D I R B Y H Z

ABBA GOLD
ABBEY ROAD
BACK IN BLACK
BAD
BAT OUT OF HELL
BELIEVE
BOSTON
BROTHERS IN ARMS
COME ON OVER
DANGEROUS
DIRTY DANCING
FAITH
GREASE
HYBRID THEORY
IN A GADDA DA VIDA
JAGGED LITTLE PILL
LED ZEPPELIN IV
METALLICA
MILLENNIUM
MUSIC BOX
NEVERMIND
NO ANGEL
NO FENCES
PRIVATE DANCER
RUMOURS
SPICEWORLD
TAPESTRY
THE BODYGUARD
THE JOSHUA TREE
THE WALL
THRILLER
TITANIC
TRUE BLUE

13. CONSTELLATIONS

L N S A Y T V U N Y V W T X P Y X I S R Z
E U C E R O T P L U C S S U S A G E P V Z
M R P A I B E F R Q A U E R R O T C I P H
U E I U R R I S S I V R C C V K Z R D Z U
L A W D S I A L M S M U S C A A G U D R F
E V Z E A M N M H N R A I U Q O R K S A S
A K U G I N S A M A A T P U P S X E S U F
C S F N C Z U V U L T T A Q R A R N P R V
R G O X E C T S T O T R G L N P E E C Z J
C R L L P U U Q U V I W Z R E M L S H S F
S N F R H P C S C U G O O N U O D U A U T
N N E O E X A Q S V A F S U G S Q R M N N
A R A F U T N S S U S Z Y S U O N D A I M
T N C T S C A T U L P Z Y P D D L Y E C A
C S J Y X L M R H P M H M O V A A H L R O
O G U F G E H A C E R I O P C R S T E I R
M E Y D C N S E U C N S S E T O O B O C C
A M X B N J U K I U A M R O N D P W N Q E
V I J P K I H S H L A T O L T I Y A O W T
F N E H F Y M R P A A N T L I A X C V Z U
S I L A D R A P O L E M A C O V E L A O S

ANTLIA
APUS
AQUARIUS
ARA
ARIES
BOOTES
CAELUM
CAMELOPARDALIS
CARINA
CEPHEUS
CETUS
CHAMAELEON
CIRCINUS
CRATER
CRUX
CYGNUS
DORADO
DRACO
ERIDANUS
FORNAX
GEMINI
GRUS
HYDRUS
INDUS
LACERTA
LEPUS
LIBRA
LUPUS
MENSA
MUSCA
NORMA
OCTANS
OPHIUCHUS SCUTUM
PAVO
PEGASUS
SCULPTOR
PERSEUS
PHOENIX
PICTOR
PISCES
PYXIS
SAGITTA
SERPENS
SEXTANS
TAURUS
TUCANA
URSA MINOR
VELA
VIRGO
VOLANS
VULPECULA

14. TYPES OF ROCK

```
S O A P S T O N E T I N I L E H P E N B S
L W P C C O D J E H P E N O T S N E E R G
L R O H H O R N F E L S G R A N I T E X O
G A A L Y E Q U A R T Z I T E C C I J R I
L L N M B L R E L B R A M U Z P U M I C E
K I D U R J L T U C U G Y P S U M O V A T
E M E G E E S I L T S T O N E G W T W E I
L E S C C T E K T J U E Y T G P F A T G S
A S I A C Y Y Q E E T P H O N O L I T E L
H T T S I H C S D I O R I T E I G D W V E
S O E E A C B A S A L T P I D O L R S N F
B N E T E A M O C E D E C B L X L F W Q B
E E T I T R H D C T L V X C I E T I N U D
T F I L I T O E N I T N E P R E S J E E E
I C R O R L R G T N E C R I V O A C T T U
T E O O O S B E S O K R A C P D J I I J S
A O N M P U B Q C Z Y F H R E B L R R A C
M A I D A T A C O N I T E I S P H I E S O
G T C I V U G B R O P E T T A P A M L P R
E C L L E F S X D M T E C E E B G T O E I
P I L U O F Z Q M I G M A T I T E S D R A
```

ANDESITE
ANORTHOSITE
APLITE
ARKOSE
BASALT
BRECCIA
CHALK
CHERT
COAL
DIATOMITE
DIORITE
DOLERITE
DOLOMITE
DUNITE
ECLOGITE
EVAPORITE
FELSITE
FLINT
GABBRO
GRANITE
GREENSTONE
GYPSUM
HORNFELS
JADEITE
JASPER
LIMESTONE
MARBLE
MARL
MIGMATITE
MONZONITE
NEPHELINITE
NORITE
OOLITE
PEGMATITE
PELITE
PHONOLITE
PHYLLITE
PICRITE
PUMICE
QUARTZITE
SCHIST
SCORIA
SERPENTINE
SHALE
SILTSTONE
SOAPSTONE
TACONITE
TEPHRITE
TRACHYTE
TUFF

15. BEST SELLING SINGLES

Q Z N T P E P S I B T D L K Z Z I T H V A
Y I W R U B W L R O W U O N W Y L O R C P
B S O E G T T V X A F E B N R H A S M E U
O F D V N I A I C I E E H F T K S Y Q C P
R L Y O U T C S T P H B V E E T K A Q T P
N E A T H E H U S T L E Y E Y R E W C Q Y
T T W O T L A R G O F V C D I J N L Y H L
O M T N C E G R W V V V W A D L U A L F O
B E C S B A M E R I C A N P I E E D N M V
E L T T O B A N I E I N E G H V T B E D E
A O M I U G Z D W A T E R L O O V G W S O
L V H G U O N E G N O R T S U L P O X Y Y
I E Y J E E F R F S A R W Q N N A R M A L
V Y G E U T M W H O K N E W D I P O N S F
E O U G N A B J Q P T S I D D Y E E E N R
J U O A Y O T A K E O N M E O Z R G R O E
T V K Y S I H D C A G T E L G A D R U M T
F E E L I N G S X K S V H N C R O Y O I T
B H S T T E S U H C A S S A M C L W J S U
P W O Q O R E D N E T E M E V O L Y M T B
M E A G A I N S T T H E M U S I C N C G G

ALWAYS
AMERICAN PIE
BEAUTIFUL
BELIEVE
BORN TO BE ALIVE
BUTTERFLY
CRAZY IN LOVE
DONT TELL ME
FEELINGS
FERNANDO
GENIE IN A BOTTLE
GET BACK
HEY JUDE
HEY YA
HONEY
HOUND DOG
HUNG UP
ITS NOT OVER
LET IT BE
LET ME LOVE YOU
LOVE ME TENDER
MACARENA
MASSACHUSETTS
ME AGAINST THE MUSIC
MY LOVE
PAPER DOLL
PUPPY LOVE
SIMON SAYS
SORRY
STRONG ENOUGH
SURRENDER
TAKE ON ME
TEDDY BEAR
THE HUSTLE
TOXIC
VOGUE
WATERLOO
WAY DOWN
WHO KNEW
YMCA

16. OPERAS

T	S	Y	U	A	T	F	D	O	N	P	A	S	Q	U	A	L	E	D	C	I
O	W	T	I	L	K	H	F	E	L	E	K	T	R	A	N	I	T	Y	E	P
D	F	D	T	J	A	T	E	A	N	V	T	O	W	J	H	E	T	C	U	U
N	A	H	N	Z	S	F	K	F	T	U	I	S	T	R	X	E	R	L	P	R
A	I	A	T	C	G	M	I	I	I	S	V	C	U	E	A	W	B	P	A	I
R	A	L	Z	J	E	R	R	S	P	E	L	A	S	A	L	H	U	G	G	T
U	A	I	Y	S	L	R	G	W	R	Y	R	A	G	E	F	L	T	T	L	A
T	A	L	R	J	U	O	O	N	V	A	B	Y	F	T	M	R	O	R	I	N
O	M	E	K	V	E	J	H	D	I	E	P	Z	A	K	J	E	Y	S	A	I
T	S	D	I	N	A	N	R	E	C	R	E	E	A	N	I	C	L	A	C	M
T	P	D	R	O	G	I	E	C	N	I	R	P	D	V	G	R	T	E	C	D
E	L	N	J	G	L	B	Y	M	O	G	A	E	H	S	E	E	W	A	I	D
L	E	A	M	A	V	A	U	M	N	V	R	A	H	S	M	H	L	H	O	U
O	S	N	A	Q	E	M	O	L	A	S	V	I	I	T	O	T	I	I	O	B
G	T	O	C	F	Q	R	W	N	M	K	U	U	N	D	R	R	L	C	C	Y
I	R	S	B	F	H	O	O	A	R	I	O	D	A	N	T	E	H	G	C	L
R	O	M	E	O	A	N	D	J	U	L	I	E	T	B	D	W	B	A	U	L
Z	Y	A	T	A	G	R	I	P	P	I	N	A	B	I	P	P	R	L	B	I
Y	E	S	H	I	K	C	E	Z	Z	O	W	T	F	U	C	M	U	O	A	B
Z	N	O	M	I	N	N	A	V	O	I	G	N	O	D	E	Y	Y	J	N	M
K	S	D	O	N	C	A	R	L	O	S	W	A	O	N	Z	T	N	D	N	A

AGRIPPINA
AIDA
ALBERT HERRING
ALCINA
ARIODANTE
BILLY BUDD
CARMEN
DON CARLOS
DON GIOVANNI
DON PASQUALE
ELEKTRA
ERNANI
FALSTAFF
FAUST
FIDELIO
I PURITANI
LAKME
LES TROYENS
LOHENGRIN
LOUISE
LULU
MACBETH
MANON
MARTHA
MIGNON
NABUCCO
NORMA
OTELLO
PAGLIACCI
PARSIFAL
PRINCE IGOR
RIGOLETTO
ROMEO AND JULIET
SALOME
SAMSON AND DELILAH
SEMELE
SERSE
THE FIERY ANGEL
TOSCA
TURANDOT
WERTHER
WOZZECK

17. EUROPEAN MAMMALS

```
I A T I Z J P O R C U P I N E L T Z O P V
O B O C A R M P E H A M S T E R A Z R E B
D N E C R E I N D E E R B E R V C A J E V
G T K X R N L P S Y L G R E Y S E A L H P
N A L E S A E W Q V V A E R G B L T X S O
L E J D O R M O U S E D H N N N O S I B T
V I T P O R P O I S E E I W E B P V Z M A
P A D R Y U Q G R O D M O A R E D F O X R
I I L T A O T S R G M R E D D E E R F N K
B H A R E M A M E E B A D G E R L U A C C
M I N K S J E H L R T S T E V H R L U T A
S U R L A W O N E U G D L I M O L E I M L
T W T J Y G T V I D Y O U N B S G P T K B
A I D M L U A X O P V X N Q K B H J H T G
R L T A B E L L E R T S I P I P A O L A O
N D C E B K P K E G R E Y S Q U I R R E L
W B E L K H P T W O O D M O U S E Z H S V
O O H G I B A C E S W I L D G O A T Q E E
R A L N C W E R H S P E R M W H A L E F L
B R I F C H I P M U N K R A C C O O N Q W
S J C W I L D C A T C O Y P U F L Y N X C
```

BADGER
BEAVER
BISON
BLACK RAT
BROWN BEAR
BROWN RAT
CHIPMUNK
COYPU
DOLPHIN
DORMOUSE
ELK
GREY SEAL
GREY SQUIRREL
HAMSTER
HARE
HEDGEHOG
HORSE
IBEX
JACKAL
KILLER WHALE
LEMMING
LYNX
MINK
MOLE
OTTER
PINE MARTEN
PIPISTRELLE BAT
POLECAT
PORCUPINE
PORPOISE
RABBIT
RACCOON
RED DEER
RED FOX
RED SQUIRREL
REINDEER
ROE DEER
SHEEP
SHREW
SPERM WHALE
STOAT
WALRUS
WATER VOLE
WEASEL
WILD BOAR
WILD GOAT
WILDCAT
WOLF
WOOD MOUSE

18. MOST WATCHED TV

O N E F O O T I N T H E G R A V E A S I R

P T C P T H E V I C A R O F D I B L E Y E

E F E M M E R D A L E T D Y Y S P Y B S I

N T H E C U C K O O W A L T Z R O M W R Z

A B E Y R T H E S W E E N E Y E P D E E A

L K A F T T I V F R E B S X J D S Y K M R

L F Y T B L S F B M A T A H U N T Y W O F

H P T C F E A N S N K R U Z S E A N Z O S

O U D H Y M S U O W I A F P T T R E J L V

U O I H P W C R S I D E I O G S S I C B I

R S H G O B L A O A T H C P O A O G Z S L

S A L L A D P O V M C A B I O E O H P E A

M A S T E R M I N D R X N D D P W B O I G

M R Q V A Q U E S T I O N O F S P O R T N

A T O U C H O F F R O S T L R X S U R N I

D O C T O R O N T H E G O C I O M R I U X

W I S H Y O U W E R E H E R E U C S D A O

L O N D O N S B U R N I N G N P E F G E B

J Z H F J I M L L F I X I T D E S L E R N

C K N A L B Y T E K N A L B S I M N B O C

B I R D S O F A F E A T H E R J F U I M R

A QUESTION OF SPORT
A TOUCH OF FROST
BIRDS OF A FEATHER
BLANKETY BLANK
BOXING ALI VS FRAZIER
BREAD
CASUALTY
CORONATION STREET
DALLAS
DOCTOR ON THE GO
EASTENDERS
EMMERDALE
HEARTBEAT
INSPECTOR MORSE
JIMLL FIX IT
JUST GOOD FRIENDS
LONDONS BURNING
MASTERMIND
MORE AUNTIES BLOOMERS
NEIGHBOURS
ONE FOOT IN THE GRAVE
OPEN ALL HOURS
POP IDOL
POPSTARS
PORRIDGE
THE CUCKOO WALTZ
THE SWEENEY
THE VICAR OF DIBLEY
WISH YOU WERE HERE

19. TREES

Q R H B Y T K X E V O R G N A M D E R E R
M L O S V Q U U D S Y J F Z O G R E D L A
C E N N Q R P N P A S Y T L A F T C A D D
O V E E B A P Y L V K R A N C W M I L E E
R K Y M L M V T E A K R I F A R C A M R C
K E L M E F X K B U W E O L C A R X D B D
W R O Y U W E C I G H B U V C C I E O E E
V N C R E F V P R I E L Q A H K L Y G R R
D K U T T Z I P C S S U E F I G A D W R Q
Q M S L H N L K H U V M S X O V W O O Y O
S S T E X U O T T I A E T G O E O U O D B
P H R K M R M P F E N Y N C T N L G D N C
B U Y D Y C Y A B I N A A S A C L L C O D
Q E H B Q L S N P A M D I V U U I A Q M G
N E E H A X R C A L O F G Y C R W S B M D
P N V C P O J K H N E B A L S A T F F I H
O N U A H E A H A E A P R I C O T I S S O
P E O E O X V P A O R D O O W D E R C R L
L P J P C D E Z P Z O R A U G A S H A E L
A S G T R A T H R L E T Y Q O E L M S P Y
R A U H R I D F M U E L O A I L O N G A M

ACACIA
ALDER
ALMOND
APPLE
APRICOT
ASH
ASPEN
AVOCADO
BALSA
BEECH
BIRCH
CACAO
CHERRY
CITRUS
CORK
DOGWOOD
DOUGLAS FIR
ELDERBERRY
ELM
EUCALYPTUS
FIG
GIANT SEQUOIA
GUAVA
HAZEL
HICKORY
HOLLY
HONEY LOCUST
HORNBEAM
LARCH
MAGNOLIA
MANGO
MAPLE
MULBERRY
MYRTLE
OAK
OLIVE
PEACH
PEAR
PERSIMMON
PINE
PLUM
POPLAR
RED CEDAR
RED MANGROVE
REDWOOD
SAGUARO
TEAK
WALNUT
WILLOW
YEW

20. GAMES & PUZZLES

```
H Y R A N O I T C I P P A K M A S U E B E
I E J M P X S L W J I G S A W K B X L V R
F Q L J T J Y N N E P A H E V O H S B S I
H U Q L H J L H A L N J J N T U E G B D A
E I U P E J R G A A O Y X H N S M Y A M T
H C L Y S T N J G N N I E R S Z A F R O I
C K N N S E A R G U I L O O J S R N C N L
R C A E J A A G R P L D R H K T B L S O O
A R S B R M M I A O I C O B W S L S A P S
E O D R S E K M I B D P B K E S E N O O G
S S R D E A F K R N R A W O U H S L M L T
D S O H B D A F A O C A N Q C R Y E L Y O
R W W E D K N S I K S I C R I W T A U T D
O O E M U R T I G D M M P S O U F L R G O
W R D R K H A A F O E S K R I N K I U E T
S D O D G U M U D H I H D I W O O O L D T
V N C U W M C L G I T P T O R N D U D K O
P M O W O S I V Y H M A D T I O G E X U D
E N G N A M G N A H T S P M O M T X U M S
C O N N E C T F O U R S O I P P F I C L V
J C Z A G B A T T L E S H I P S S T H F C
```

ANAGRAMS
BACKGAMMON
BAGATELLE
BATTLESHIPS
CHESS
CLUEDO
CODEWORDS
CONNECT FOUR
DOMINOES
DOT TO DOT
DOWNFALL
DRAUGHTS
GUESS WHO
HANGMAN
HANIDOKU
HITORI
JENGA
JIGSAW
KAKURO
LUDO
MAH JONGG
MARBLES
MASYU
MONOPOLY
NOUGHTS AND CROSSES
NURIKABE
OTHELLO
PATHFINDER
PICTIONARY
POLYWORD
QUICK CROSSWORD
RISK
SCRABBLE
SHOVE HAPENNY
SOLITAIRE
SPOT THE DIFFERENCE
SUDOKU
TRIONIMOS
WORDSEARCH

Anagrams

Use your general knowledge of the given subject to work out the 10 jumbled-up words in each category

1

PRECIOUS STONES

EAT MYTHS

□□□□□□□□

ZIP LULL ASIA

□□□□□ □□□□□□

SONNET MOO

□□□□□□□□□

OUT SQUIRE

□□□□□□□□□

OUR ESQ TZAR

□□□□ □□□□□□

TO PRIDE

□□□□□□□

OUT MINERAL

□□□□□□□□□□

I PERHAPS

□□□□□□□□

HAD CYCLONE

□□□□□□□□□□

BOT NOODLES

□□□□□□□□□□

2

BUTTERFLIES

WAIL ALL SWOT

☐☐☐☐☐☐☐☐☐☐☐

DARE ARM LID

☐☐☐ ☐☐☐☐☐☐☐

TYPE ALADDIN

☐☐☐☐☐☐☐ ☐☐☐☐

ELIOT HOLSTERS

☐☐☐☐☐☐☐☐☐☐☐☐☐

COKE CAP

☐☐☐☐☐☐☐

TRILL FAIRY

☐☐☐☐☐☐☐☐☐☐

WOW DOBERMAN

☐☐☐☐☐☐ ☐☐☐☐☐

CAM HORN

☐☐☐☐☐☐☐

DUNE IS BOLA

☐☐☐☐☐☐ ☐☐☐☐

BEIGE BACH TAW

☐☐☐☐☐☐☐ ☐☐☐☐☐

3

BBC SPORTS PERSONALITIES OF THE YEAR

JAG ECHO ZEAL

□□□ □□□□□□□□

I ZIP ALL HARPS

□□□□ □□□□□□□□□

FORFEND WILT FAN

□□□□□□ □□□□□□□□

LEK HEM LYSOL

□□□□□ □□□□□□

KNOWS ONLY JINN

□□□□□ □□□□□□□□□

A A DUFF CALLIPER

□□□□□ □□□□□□□□□

VIM BACKED HAD

□□□□□ □□□□□□□

GRAVED EVEREST

□□□□□ □□□□□□□□

NIXON WELLES

□□□□□□ □□□□□

WACO HEMLINE

□□□□□□□ □□□□

4

FAMOUS ARTISTS

VET CHANGING NOV

SEA DRAGGED

DOCUMENT ALE

I DIVA DOLLARS

VEND CARD HUM

CANAL PUN ZEE

POP SOB CALAIS

SIR MAINSHEET

MAJOR ION

FOG ANY CORSICA

5

CHEESES

MEAN MELT

ACT MEMBER

FOR QUOTER

LIE HUSBAND

NO LOG OR ZAG

ROMANCE ASP

ALLEY SWEDEN

DISCRETE LEER

CAR JET MONKEY

EGO LEE CLOUDBURST

6

OLYMPIC EVENTS

ATM NO BIND

NEWT GIRLS

TEAR SEQUIN

SOH BIG BEL

HE ICY COKE

IN SETTLE BAN

AWOKEN TOD

LATIN ROTH

STINGY SCAM

TWIG FILE NIGHT

7

PRIME MINISTERS

POLER BERET

I TWILIT LAMP

CATTLE ELEMENT

DOWNHILL SOAR

HATH DARED WE

BORN ITALY

A BRAW LANDOWNER

ANNOYED THEN

NIL BY WASTELAND

MANACLE LASH JAG

8

BIRDS OF PREY

TWO WANLY

□□□□□ □□□

WOK HAGS

□□□□□□□

LEG LED ABA

□□□□ □□□□□

REST ELK

□□□□□□□

A SIR HARM HERR

□□□□□ □□□□□□□

LE TURVU

□□□□□□□

ZAB DURZ

□□□□□□□

OCHRE CLEWS

□□□□□□□ □□□

WOW SHARP ARK

□□□□□□□□□□

RACY BESTIRRED

□□□□□□□□□ □□□□

9

TYPES OF CLOTHING

ANGERED US

□□□□□□□□□

DIE COB

□□□□□□

ORGANS

□□□□□□

ACRID NAG

□□□□□□□□

DOLE ART

□□□□□□□

AS A TWO TIC

□□□□□□□□□

HI MAN PAS

□□□□□□□□

SUB LOON

□□□□□□□

TOELESS TAP

□□□□□□□□□□

HAPLESS PRUDE

□□□□□ □□□□□□□

10

VARIETIES OF FRUIT

CREATE INN

☐☐☐☐☐☐☐☐☐

OGEE MANTRAP

☐☐☐☐☐☐☐☐☐☐☐

A RUN TWITCHER

☐☐☐☐☐ ☐☐☐☐☐☐☐

TRY WARS REB

☐☐☐☐☐☐☐☐☐☐

EGG GENERA

☐☐☐☐☐☐☐☐☐

AGE OLD BORON

☐☐☐☐☐ ☐☐☐☐☐☐

NEPAL PIPE

☐☐☐☐☐☐☐☐☐

MOP MINERS

☐☐☐☐☐☐☐☐☐

DRAM NINA

☐☐☐☐☐☐☐☐

PAD OVA OR ACE

☐☐☐☐☐☐☐ ☐☐☐☐

11

SHAKESPEAREAN CHARACTERS

GIBBON OR ELK

□□□□□□□□□□□

OR UNSOCIAL

□□□□□□□□□□

ODD SEAMEN

□□□□□□□□□

DARNED FIN

□□□□□□□□□

INSURGENT LED

□□□□□□□□□□□□

TERN ON CZARS

□□□□□□□□□□□

HOUSTON TEC

□□□□□□□□□□

TEA BASINS

□□□□□□□□□

TURN EIDERS

□□□□□□□□□

NORSE BABU

□□□□□□□□□

12

MEDICAL EQUIPMENT

UNIQUE TORT

□□□□□□□□□□

DAISY CHAIN MILES

□□□□□□□□ □□□□□□□

ORB FIELD TRIAL

□□□□□□□□□□□□□

TEST POOCHES

□□□□□□□□□□□

COSMIC PORE

□□□□□□□□□□

MY SAXON KEG

□□□□□□ □□□□

PIER OR TARS

□□□□□□□□□□

THREES CRT

□□□□□□□□□

RAP ME CAKE

□□□□□□□□□

INTERVAL TO

□□□□□□□□□□

13

WELL-KNOWN MONSTERS

HAVE LATIN

□□□□□□□□□

QUASH ACTS

□□□□□□□□□

KNIFE TANNERS

□□□□□□□□□□□□

FEW LOWER

□□□□□□□□

UNTO MIRA

□□□□□□□□

PRIM AVE

□□□□□□□

BE CURSER

□□□□□□□□

RICE HAM

□□□□□□□

ZIG ALL DO

□□□□□□□□

ONTO MOCKERIES

□□□□□□ □□□□□□□

14

HERBS, SPICES AND SEASONINGS

PEN CREEPY PEAN

□□□□□□□ □□□□□□

A MARS MALAGA

□□□□□ □□□□□□

ARCADE AS YEW

□□□□□□□ □□□□

ARMLESS NOG

□□□□□□□□□□

A TIDE A SOFA

□□□□□□□□□□

ANT ARISES

□□□□ □□□□□

REFUGE KEN

□□□□□□□□□

OHM MALICE

□□□□□□□□□

BECK PER LAPP

□□□□□ □□□□□□

A MAD CORM

□□□□□□□□

15

INSECT SPECIES

MY ASPIRING ANT

□□□□□□□ □□□□□□

AN ELF CRY

□□□□□ □□□

HER PROPS SAG

□□□□□□□□□□□

LISPING RAT

□□□□□□□□□□

A RELUCTANT EFT

□□□□□□□□□□ □□□

OF CAR CHECK

□□□□□□□□□□

BULLET TO BE

□□□□□□□□□□

DEFY MALLS

□□□□□□□□□

POL FREE HAP

□□□□□□□□□□

LICE GNAW

□□□□□□□□

16

UK FOOTBALL CLUBS

VERB LURK CARBONS

SIBYL TRICOT

A SPECTRAL CLAY

NEED ITUNE DUD

DISLODGE RHUMB

HEREUNTO I SUMS

ERRORS AVERMENT

RUM HOT SPOT

BIN AN HEIR

ETERNITY LOON

17

THEATRICAL TERMS

CATEGORISED TIN

☐☐☐☐☐ ☐☐☐☐☐☐☐☐☐

NO FOURTHS FOE

☐☐☐☐☐ ☐☐ ☐☐☐☐☐

DEIGN ALL DAY

☐☐☐☐☐☐☐ ☐☐☐☐

NURSED DUTY

☐☐☐☐☐☐☐☐☐☐

FARTHEST GIG

☐☐☐☐☐ ☐☐☐☐☐☐

SING THRIFT

☐☐☐☐☐ ☐☐☐☐☐

LOUNGE MOO

☐☐☐☐☐☐☐☐☐

CASKET BAG

☐☐☐☐☐☐☐☐☐

PIN HASTE

☐☐☐☐☐☐☐☐

LINT ACCRUAL

☐☐☐☐☐☐☐ ☐☐☐☐

18

FISH SPECIES

BASKET CLICK

□□□□□□□□□□□

WORN TURBOT

□□□□□ □□□□□

ARC PRIM ORR

□□□□□□ □□□□

WISH FORDS

□□□□□□□□□

NOEL MOLES

□□□□□ □□□□

A CAD ABURR

□□□□□□□□□

FINKS OHM

□□□□ □□□□

DRY J HOON

□□□□ □□□□

OR FUN LED

□□□□□□□□

NORSE TUG

□□□□□□□□

19

LONDON AVENUE OF STARS

THEBES TALE

□□□ □□□□□□□

BY RELISHES SAY

□□□□□□□ □□□□□□

UNLOVELIER ERICA

□□□□□□□□ □□□□□□□

CACKLED FROTH CHI

□□□□□□ □□□□□□□□□

AGEISM MIGHT

□□□□□□ □□□□□

VERMONT OLD CARD

□□□□□□ □□□□□□□□

HER HELICOPTERS

□□□□□□□□□□□ □□□

SHOW RETENTION

□□□ □□□ □□□□□□□

FORGOTTEN MANY

□□□□□□ □□□□□□□

CHOKY CANTON

□□□□ □□□□□□□

20

WINE VARIETIES

MOTIONAL LAD

□□□□□□□□□□□

CENSURED HOOT

□□□□□ □□ □□□□□

CHIC DEVOIR

□□□□□□□□□□

ISLAND FEZ

□□□□□□□□□

IN PORTION

□□□□□ □□□□

HAND CRAYON

□□□□□□□□□□

PEG CAN HAM

□□□□□□□□□

USE OIL JABA

□□□□□□□□□□

CASTE MUD

□□□□□□□□

I ROC BEERS

□□□□□□□□□

Polyword

Using the given letters no more than once, make as many words as possible of four or more letters, always including the central letter.
Capitalised words and plurals are disallowed. You can also make one word using all the nine available letters.

1

How did you rate?
26 words - Average
31 words - Good
37 words - Very good
41 words - Excellent

2

How did you rate?
28 words - Average
33 words - Good
39 words - Very good
45 words - Excellent

3

How did you rate?
28 words - Average
33 words - Good
39 words - Very good
44 words - Excellent

4

How did you rate?
26 words - Average
31 words - Good
37 words - Very good
41 words - Excellent

5

How did you rate?
28 words - Average
33 words - Good
39 words - Very good
45 words - Excellent

6

How did you rate?
25 words - Average
29 words - Good
34 words - Very good
39 words - Excellent

7

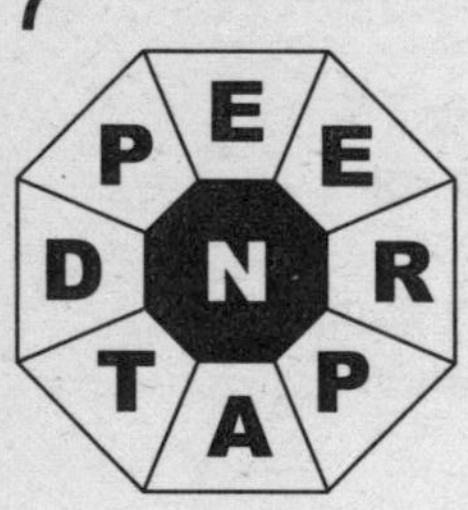

How did you rate?
34 words - Average
41 words - Good
47 words - Very good
54 words - Excellent

8

How did you rate?
18 words - Average
21 words - Good
24 words - Very good
28 words - Excellent

9

How did you rate?
32 words - Average
38 words - Good
44 words - Very good
50 words - Excellent

10

How did you rate?
15 words - Average
18 words - Good
21 words - Very good
23 words - Excellent

11

How did you rate?
25 words - Average
29 words - Good
34 words - Very good
39 words - Excellent

12

How did you rate?
34 words - Average
41 words - Good
47 words - Very good
54 words - Excellent

13

How did you rate?
33 words - Average
39 words - Good
45 words - Very good
51 words - Excellent

14

How did you rate?
20 words - Average
24 words - Good
27 words - Very good
32 words - Excellent

15

How did you rate?
28 words - Average
33 words - Good
39 words - Very good
44 words - Excellent

16

How did you rate?
32 words - Average
38 words - Good
44 words - Very good
50 words - Excellent

17

How did you rate?
18 words - Average
21 words - Good
24 words - Very good
28 words - Excellent

18

How did you rate?
28 words - Average
33 words - Good
39 words - Very good
45 words - Excellent

19

How did you rate?
29 words - Average
34 words - Good
40 words - Very good
46 words - Excellent

20

How did you rate?
26 words - Average
31 words - Good
37 words - Very good
41 words - Excellent

The Solutions

1 Letter Logic

W	R	E	S	T	L	E	D		S	C	O	R	C	H	E	D
			P				E		I				O			
I	S	L	E		S	K	A	T	E		W	A	R	M	T	H
	H		L		P		R		V		A		S		R	
B	A	L	L	O	O	N		B	E	A	R		A	L	O	E
	M				O		D				R		G		T	
	P		S	C	R	E	E		S	N	I	D	E		T	
	O		P				C		W		O				E	
B	O	D	I	C	E		O	N	E		R	O	T	A	R	Y
			N		N		R		A				A			
S	H	O	E		Q	U	A	R	T	E	R		S	I	C	K
	I				U		T				O		T		L	
	N		S	P	I	K	E		B	O	M	B	E		O	
	D		C		R				E		A				V	
G	U	R	U		E	A	S	T	E	R	N		B	E	E	F
			L				T		T		C		O			
M	I	L	L	E	R		O	A	R		E	G	O	I	S	M
	N				E		R		O				S		E	
	S		P	A	S	T	E		O	U	G	H	T		R	
	P		R		T				T		R				I	
M	I	N	I		O	O	Z	E		T	A	L	L	B	O	Y
	R		V		R		E		E		S		U		U	
S	E	S	A	M	E		B	A	S	I	S		N	O	S	E
			T				R		P				C			
S	W	E	E	T	P	E	A		Y	O	U	T	H	F	U	L

2 Letter Logic

P	H	Y	S	I	C	A	L		S	H	E	E	P	D	I	P
			M				E		E				L			
I	S	L	E		S	T	A	I	R		S	H	A	B	B	Y
	T		L		I		K		V		A		C		O	
F	A	I	L	U	R	E		B	E	A	R		A	W	R	Y
	M				E		R				D		R		D	
	I		P	E	N	C	E		C	H	I	L	D		E	
	N		R				P		A		N				R	
C	A	V	I	A	R		H	U	T		E	X	C	E	S	S
			N		U		R		C				U			
P	A	C	T		F	E	A	T	H	E	R		R	U	S	H
	R				F		S				E		R		A	
	G		S	H	I	N	E		A	N	G	R	Y		L	
	U		T		A				I		U				T	
V	E	T	O		N	A	T	U	R	A	L		P	O	S	T
			N				O		C		A		U			
A	T	H	E	N	S		T	A	R		R	E	L	I	S	H
	R				P		E		A				S		U	
	E		S	T	O	R	M		F	I	B	R	E		P	
	M		W		N				T		L				R	
C	O	K	E		S	E	C	T		L	I	N	S	E	E	D
	L		A		O		R		F		S		P		M	
F	O	S	T	E	R		A	T	L	A	S		I	D	E	A
			E				S		O				K			
B	A	R	R	A	C	K	S		P	A	T	H	E	T	I	C

3 Letter Logic

P	A	T	C	H		V	I	S	O	R		S	N	A	I	L
A		H		O		E		L		O		Q		B		A
C	R	U	M	P	E	T		U	N	T	R	U	T	H		C
K		M		E				M		U		A		O		E
A	M	B	O		S	T	U	B		N	O	T	A	R	Y	
G				S		A		E		D						L
E	G	Y	P	T		B	A	R	N		A	D	M	I	R	E
		O		I		O				C		I		N		S
Y	O	U		C	R	O	W	B	A	R		S	A	C	K	S
O		N		K				E		I		T		L		E
D	I	G	S		I	D	L	E		M	O	R	T	I	S	E
E				H		O		K		I		A		N		
L	I	T	R	E		O	C	E	A	N		C	H	E	S	T
		O		X		R		E		A		T				A
C	O	M	P	A	S	S		P	O	L	O		S	T	A	R
H		B		G		T		E				A		I		O
O	D	O	U	R		E	A	R	P	L	U	G		G	U	T
I		L		A		P				U		E		E		
C	L	A	M	M	Y		P	R	E	P		N	O	R	T	H
E						P		E		I		T				O
	B	A	N	A	N	A		T	I	N	Y		I	M	P	S
N		I		P		R		H				P		A		I
O		M	A	R	T	I	N	I		F	I	A	N	C	E	E
V		E		O		S		N		U		S		A		R
A	U	D	E	N		H	I	K	E	R		T	A	W	N	Y

4 Letter Logic

P	R	O	S	P	E	C	T		M	A	N	D	A	R	I	N
			N				O		I				T			
Y	O	Y	O		D	R	A	I	N		U	N	H	O	O	K
	V		U		R		D		C		P		E		R	
H	E	A	T	H	E	R		L	E	N	S		I	T	C	H
	R				G		A				T		S		H	
	F		S	U	S	H	I		S	H	A	F	T		A	
	E		H				R		A		R				R	
A	D	V	E	R	B		F	A	T		T	R	E	N	D	Y
			E		A		O		I				J			
D	E	A	N		P	I	R	A	N	H	A		E	A	R	L
	A				T		C				L		C		I	
	S		S	L	I	M	E		S	P	R	A	T		V	
	E		I		S				H		E				A	
O	D	D	S		T	A	P	I	O	C	A		S	O	L	O
			A				I		R		D		A			
M	U	L	L	E	D		C	A	T		Y	E	L	L	E	D
	T				U		O		E				T		N	
	I		Y	A	C	H	T		S	U	R	L	Y		T	
	L		A		H				T		O				H	
L	I	A	R		E	A	S	T		O	B	V	I	O	U	S
	T		D		S		H		H		I		R		S	
B	Y	P	A	S	S		A	C	O	R	N		O	P	E	N
			G				W		O				N			
E	M	M	E	N	T	A	L		P	L	A	T	Y	P	U	S

5 Letter Logic

PASSWORD FLAGPOLE
O O L I
HERB SCORE JACKET
Y E E M S U A N
DEPRIVE CHIP SAVE
B E B I S I
R CIRCA MOTTO O
O A T A E U
SWATHE HAT RELISH
C N R C I
RASH CROCHET MOSS
L H O O B A
P SWARM INTRO Y
H E N N A S
RASP TEARFUL STOW
I P A L I
IMPACT TIN YELLOW
O E L T L C
R CRAZY RUSTY T
O O C Y T U
SCUT ACRE BAGPIPE
C T K A F V R L
ROTATE VALUE IBEX
G E I N
NINETEEN TOMATOES

6 Letter Logic

CABIN CRASS SHARD
H U E U N C T G A
ANIMATE TERRIER C
B L R E E L E E
LADY OMEN ASLEEP
I T O N M D
SNAKE COAL PSYCHE
N A H F P U G
COG STARTLE LOSER
O E E A A U T E
RARE PEAR RATRACE
K B L P L T R
SOMME ERASE ELDER
I V P U S R O
SCREECH LUSH STAG
A A R A I K I U
COCOA NINEPIN ALE
H L G T A I R
ELEVEN PROP FEAST
T M A E E E
ASTHMA MARE EDAM
A M A T P F I P
T AUSTRIA TRAINEE
O R T O N O S G S
MITRE NUTTY TROUT

7 Letter Logic

SHOP PARABLE SEWN
U A E A A B P I
ETON NIGHT BRAINY
C T C E H N C
CHRONIC TELEVISED
M L C R E
SPOIL DARWIN LUDO
O M M U A E A
SLOE OBTUSE SMIRK
I O I T B E L
LONDON ONE RUSTIC
E S U I S N
ZINC TASTING ALGA
N E O C A G
CANNON EWE DRENCH
N C E T C I R
VINYL CHARGE SLUG
T S E E R T S
CYST CEREAL MATHS
H A M F R
ESPIONAGE BOMBAST
U S R R R O K
INSTEP ADORE ARID
N L I V B S R L
BYTE PREFECT DULL

8 Letter Logic

HIFI AMNESTY SIGH
C N N A U E U R
DIRT TRIBE SPREAD
N R H L D F P
IGNITED NEWSPAPER
C M B E C
SCRAP MARBLE EASY
H T S C E D U
HIDE TITBIT AFIRE
N A E N G E R
MALLET RUG LOAFER
A E I I T A
AMPS SEASONS HOLY
A A M B T E
ENIGMA BUS EUROPE
A N N R T N L
STEEP VOYAGE SNAG
E C W C D H T
PEST LONELY BAGEL
E I E M M
OSTEOPATH HOWEVER
M N A G B L A
COBALT KHAKI EGGS
K G O E L L S L
FETE PANCAKE SUET

9 Letter Logic

```
S E P A L ■ B R A S S ■ D E N I M
E ■ L ■ E ■ A ■ N ■ T ■ R ■ I ■ A
Q U A F F E D ■ A I R W A V E ■ I
U ■ T ■ T ■ ■ ■ E ■ I ■ M ■ C ■ D
I R O N ■ S C A M ■ C L A R E T ■
N ■ ■ ■ B ■ O ■ I ■ T ■ ■ ■ ■ ■ A
S U G A R ■ B O A T ■ A B A C U S
■ ■ L ■ I ■ R ■ ■ ■ T ■ L ■ A ■ W
P E A ■ S N A F F L E ■ O U T D O
O ■ S ■ K ■ ■ ■ O ■ A ■ W ■ E ■ O
L I S T ■ B A I L ■ S A F F R O N
K ■ ■ ■ K ■ N ■ K ■ P ■ I ■ E ■ ■
A M P L E ■ A U D I O ■ S T R A W
■ ■ R ■ E ■ C ■ A ■ O ■ H ■ ■ ■ I
S C O R P I O ■ N I N E ■ U S E D
O ■ M ■ S ■ N ■ C ■ ■ ■ B ■ H ■ E
V I O L A ■ D R E S S E R ■ I N N
I ■ T ■ K ■ A ■ ■ ■ W ■ U ■ R ■ ■
E L E V E N ■ R A V E ■ T W E E D
T ■ ■ ■ ■ ■ A ■ R ■ A ■ E ■ ■ ■ E
■ G L O B A L ■ T U R F ■ E V I L
B ■ O ■ E ■ W ■ D ■ ■ ■ P ■ O ■ I
A ■ L U G G A G E ■ K I L L I N G
T ■ L ■ A ■ Y ■ C ■ I ■ U ■ C ■ H
H A Y D N ■ S T O U T ■ S W E E T
```

10 Letter Logic

```
G R O W ■ I N J E C T S ■ N U L L
■ A ■ E ■ M ■ A ■ A ■ U ■ U ■ L ■
K I W I ■ M O D E M ■ M A M M A L
■ S ■ R ■ U ■ E ■ E ■ ■ ■ E ■ M ■
B E D D I N G ■ S O U R C R E A M
■ ■ ■ N ■ E ■ M ■ ■ ■ O ■ A ■ ■ ■
A G L E T ■ C A R E S S ■ L E S S
■ O ■ S ■ P ■ T ■ M ■ E ■ ■ ■ E ■
F U S S ■ R A T T A N ■ E S S A Y
■ D ■ ■ ■ E ■ R ■ I ■ T ■ A ■ W ■
S A D I S T ■ E E L ■ R E V I E W
■ ■ ■ C ■ T ■ S ■ ■ ■ A ■ I ■ E ■
A C N E ■ I N S U L I N ■ N U D E
■ O ■ B ■ E ■ ■ ■ A ■ S ■ G ■ ■ ■
O B S E S S ■ F L U ■ I N S I S T
■ B ■ R ■ T ■ U ■ G ■ E ■ ■ ■ T ■
A L I G N ■ O R P H A N ■ S O R E
■ E ■ ■ ■ U ■ Z ■ T ■ T ■ T ■ O ■
W R A P ■ S K E W E R ■ T R I P E
■ ■ ■ E ■ E ■ ■ ■ R ■ T ■ A ■ ■ ■
R E P R O D U C E ■ J U S T I C E
■ L ■ C ■ ■ ■ U ■ J ■ T ■ A ■ H ■
E F F E C T ■ P H O N E ■ G R A N
■ I ■ N ■ O ■ I ■ K ■ E ■ E ■ P ■
K N I T ■ G O D D E S S ■ M A S T
```

11 Letter Logic

```
S A G O ■ S C E P T R E ■ T U S K
■ B ■ P ■ W ■ P ■ R ■ F ■ U ■ N ■
C A P E ■ A R I S E ■ T H R O A T
■ S ■ R ■ Y ■ C ■ N ■ ■ ■ B ■ R ■
S E D A T E D ■ A D H E S I V E S
■ ■ ■ T ■ D ■ B ■ ■ ■ L ■ N ■ ■ ■
B A S I C ■ M A R I N A ■ E A S Y
■ B ■ V ■ T ■ C ■ M ■ N ■ ■ ■ T ■
J O K E ■ R I T U A L ■ B A K E R
■ V ■ ■ ■ I ■ E ■ G ■ C ■ S ■ R ■
H E C T I C ■ R Y E ■ A B S E I L
■ ■ ■ O ■ K ■ I ■ ■ ■ R ■ U ■ L ■
H E I R ■ S E A S I D E ■ A P E X
■ Q ■ N ■ T ■ ■ ■ N ■ T ■ G ■ ■ ■
C U R A T E ■ A C T ■ A G E N C Y
■ I ■ D ■ R ■ M ■ R ■ K ■ ■ ■ R ■
E N J O Y ■ O B L I G E ■ S H E D
■ O ■ ■ ■ W ■ L ■ G ■ R ■ P ■ T ■
E X A M ■ A V E N U E ■ B I P E D
■ ■ ■ A ■ S ■ ■ ■ E ■ C ■ N ■ ■ ■
B L A S P H E M E ■ N O V E L T Y
■ A ■ O ■ ■ ■ A ■ Z ■ F ■ L ■ R ■
I R O N E D ■ G R I E F ■ E X I T
■ V ■ R ■ U ■ I ■ N ■ E ■ S ■ B ■
H A Z Y ■ B I C Y C L E ■ S E E P
```

12 Letter Logic

```
C R A S S ■ T O R U S ■ S O L A R
H ■ L ■ K ■ I ■ E ■ T ■ U ■ A ■ A
A V A R I C E ■ A M A T E U R ■ G
S ■ R ■ P ■ ■ ■ C ■ N ■ D ■ K ■ S
S U M P ■ S W A T ■ C H E E S E ■
I ■ ■ ■ B ■ H ■ O ■ E ■ ■ ■ ■ ■ G
S C O N E ■ A W R Y ■ V E S P E R
■ ■ U ■ A ■ L ■ ■ ■ S ■ X ■ L ■ E
P A N ■ S L E I G H T ■ O R A T E
I ■ C ■ T ■ ■ ■ Y ■ E ■ R ■ T ■ N
T O E S ■ C L A M ■ R A C K E T S
C ■ ■ ■ C ■ U ■ N ■ L ■ I ■ A ■ ■
H O M E R ■ K H A K I ■ S Q U I B
■ ■ A ■ E ■ E ■ S ■ N ■ M ■ ■ ■ E
J A C K D A W ■ T O G A ■ A C H E
E ■ B ■ I ■ A ■ I ■ ■ ■ T ■ U ■ F
S C E N T ■ R E C E I V E ■ P L Y
T ■ T ■ O ■ M ■ ■ ■ S ■ E ■ I ■ ■
E X H O R T ■ N E W S ■ T U D O R
R ■ ■ ■ ■ ■ U ■ N ■ U ■ H ■ ■ ■ E
■ M O H A I R ■ S T E P ■ G R I T
A ■ S ■ D ■ G ■ N ■ ■ ■ O ■ A ■ I
L ■ C H O L E R A ■ D E N I Z E N
M ■ A ■ R ■ N ■ R ■ U ■ U ■ O ■ U
S U R G E ■ T R E A D ■ S P R E E
```

13 Letter Logic

J	U	M	P		P	I	C	K	A	X	E		L	A	S	T
	N		L		L		L		R		L		A		H	
O	F	F	A		I	R	A	T	E		M	O	R	T	A	R
	E		Y		A		W		N				G		L	
E	D	I	T	I	N	G		B	A	N	Q	U	E	T	E	D
			H		T		M				U		S			
B	A	S	I	L		H	A	V	A	N	A		S	E	T	T
	G		N		S		G		S		Y				R	
W	I	N	G		H	E	A	R	S	E		C	R	E	E	K
	L				O		Z		A		O		E		F	
R	E	S	C	U	E		I	V	Y		S	L	A	L	O	M
				O	M		N				T		C		I	
A	B	U	T		A	B	E	T	T	O	R		T	O	L	L
	R		E		K				W		A		O			
B	A	R	R	I	E		P	R	O		C	E	R	I	S	E
	V		I		R		A		T		I				P	
G	A	V	E	L		U	N	D	I	E	S		S	W	A	G
	D				V		D		M		M		C		C	
S	O	U	P		E	N	A	M	E	L		T	H	I	E	F
			R		I				R		R		N			
S	A	T	E	L	L	I	T	E		M	E	D	I	A	T	E
	C		C				R		M		V		T		E	
A	R	T	I	S	T		A	G	A	P	E		Z	I	N	C
	E		S		E		S		C		R		E		O	
I	S	L	E		A	T	H	L	E	T	E		L	Y	N	X

14 Letter Logic

H	U	S	K	Y		S	A	T	Y	R		P	O	L	A	R
A		A		A		T		R		O		L		I		I
L	A	M	P	R	E	Y		A	D	A	M	A	N	T		T
C		B		N				P		R		Z		R		Z
Y	E	A	R		T	R	U	E		E	R	A	S	E	R	
O				R		E		Z		D						L
N	U	R	S	E		L	E	E	K		I	G	U	A	N	A
		E		V		I				R		R		N		R
L	O	G		E	X	C	L	U	D	E		A	P	T	L	Y
A		A		L				N		S		T		E		N
T	I	L	E		K	I	W	I		E	Q	U	I	N	O	X
C				J		N		V		T		I		N		
H	Y	E	N	A		F	L	E	E	T		T	R	A	D	E
		R		M		O		R		L		Y				A
C	R	O	W	B	A	R		S	H	E	D		G	O	A	T
R		S		O		M		A				C		M		E
O	S	I	E	R		A	T	L	A	N	T	A		E	O	N
A		O		E		L				O		C		G		
K	E	N	N	E	L		C	H	U	M		T	I	A	R	A
Y						S		O		A		I				M
	S	K	E	T	C	H		R	I	D	E		I	D	E	A
H		H		A		R		A				P		A		T
E		A	I	L	M	E	N	T		A	I	R	L	I	N	E
R		K		O		W		I		S		I		S		U
O	N	I	O	N		D	R	O	O	P		M	A	Y	O	R

15 Letter Logic

M	A	G	A	Z	I	N	E		L	I	B	E	R	A	T	E
			C				L		A				E			
S	P	A	R		C	H	A	I	R		S	A	F	A	R	I
	E		I		I		N		G		T		U		E	
G	R	I	D	D	L	E		B	E	T	A		G	N	A	T
	G				I		J				T		E		L	
	O		F	L	A	R	E		S	H	I	R	E		I	
	L		L				A		T		O				S	
B	A	B	O	O	N		L	E	O		N	U	G	G	E	T
			A		E		O		A				R			
B	A	I	T		A	Q	U	A	T	I	C		A	S	K	S
	M				R		S				H		F		O	
	P		B	E	E	F	Y		E	X	A	C	T		A	
	L		A		S				X		R				L	
H	E	R	D		T	A	P	I	O	C	A		B	E	A	D
			G				E		R		D		I			
C	I	N	E	M	A		A	R	C		E	R	N	E	S	T
	M				R		C		I				G		I	
	P		A	N	T	R	E		S	A	L	V	O		L	
	L		M		I				M		E				E	
C	A	G	E		C	L	A	M		P	A	C	K	I	N	G
	N		R		L		I		F		S		R		C	
A	T	T	I	R	E		S	H	A	L	E		A	G	E	D
			C				L		W				F			
C	O	M	A	T	O	S	E		N	I	C	O	T	I	N	E

16 Letter Logic

F	L	U	X		M	I	S	T	A	K	E		B	E	A	K
	E		Y		I		C		N		L		A		W	
B	A	I	L		S	L	A	C	K		K	I	T	B	A	G
	S		O		F		R		L				H		K	
D	E	S	P	A	I	R		S	E	V	E	N	T	E	E	N
		H			T		W				A		U			
B	A	T	O	N		B	A	R	B	E	R		B	A	S	E
	B		N		L		R		A		N				P	
B	A	N	E		A	S	P	I	R	E		C	A	B	A	L
	C				Z		L		G		B		R		T	
S	K	I	M	P	Y		A	W	E		A	R	T	F	U	L
			A		B		N				B		I		L	
L	A	I	R		O	V	E	R	J	O	Y		S	H	A	M
	N		Q		N				E		G		A			
B	E	M	U	S	E		H	E	W		R	U	N	O	U	T
	M		E		S		A		E		A				N	
C	O	M	E	T		M	U	S	L	I	N		W	A	I	L
	N				P		N		L		D		R		T	
N	E	W	S		O	U	T	L	E	T		C	I	D	E	R
			C		L				R		R		S			
W	A	R	E	H	O	U	S	E		C	E	N	T	U	R	Y
	R		P				O		S		C		B		O	
J	E	S	T	E	R		N	I	E	C	E		A	B	U	T
	N		R		I		I		R		D		N		G	
B	A	L	E		M	A	C	H	E	T	E		D	I	E	T

17 Letter Logic

P	A	L	M		B	A	C	K	L	O	G		C	O	S	Y
	R		O		O		O		A		A		O		U	
G	O	A	T		A	D	D	E	R		P	A	R	I	S	H
	M		O		T		E		V				R		H	
B	A	R	R	I	E	R		D	A	R	E	D	E	V	I	L
			B		R		S				T		C			
A	T	T	I	C		F	A	L	C	O	N		T	U	T	U
	I		K		P		U		O		A				R	
C	A	V	E		I	N	C	O	M	E		B	R	E	A	D
	R				G		E		E		R		E		P	
L	A	P	D	O	G		P	A	T		E	X	C	E	E	D
			A		Y		A				F		Y		Z	
P	L	A	Y		B	A	N	D	A	G	E		C	H	E	F
	E		T		A				D		C		L			
L	O	T	I	O	N		P	O	D		T	R	E	N	C	H
	P		M		K		E		I		O				R	
C	A	D	E	T		C	A	N	T	E	R		I	T	E	M
	R				S		R		I		Y		N		P	
E	D	G	E		W	I	L	L	O	W		A	S	S	E	T
			L		A				N		B		P			
L	I	V	E	S	T	O	C	K		T	A	K	E	O	F	F
	G		G				R		F		T		C		O	
B	L	E	A	C	H		A	D	O	P	T		T	E	R	N
	O		N		E		T		R		L		O		C	
B	O	O	T		W	R	E	S	T	L	E		R	E	E	F

18 Letter Logic

S	A	G	E		C	O	M	F	R	E	Y		B	A	T	H
	N		Y		O		I		I		A		U		H	
L	I	M	E		T	O	N	I	C		M	A	R	T	Y	R
	S		B		T		T		E				D		M	
T	E	A	R	O	O	M		P	R	I	M	R	O	S	E	S
			I		N		P				A		C			
U	S	A	G	E		S	A	U	C	E	R		K	E	P	I
	P		H		C		N		R		E				A	
P	I	N	T		O	S	P	R	E	Y		S	C	O	P	E
	C				R		I		S		F		A		R	
N	E	R	O	L	I		P	A	S		L		R		I	
			R		A		E				A		A		K	
M	A	C	E		N	O	S	E	B	A	G		W	O	A	D
	C		G		D				E		E		A			
	O		A		E		S	I	R		O	X	Y	G	E	N
	N		N		R		E		G		L				L	
P	I	C	O	T		S	E	S	A	M	E		W	A	F	T
	T				C		D		M		T		H		I	
B	E	A	M		H	Y	S	S	O	P		S	E	N	N	A
			U		E				T		C		A			
G	O	O	S	E	F	O	O	T		L	E	T	T	U	C	E
	Z		T				C		D		L		M		U	
M	O	S	A	I	C		C	H	I	V	E		E	M	M	Y
	N		R		U		U		L		R		A		I	
M	E	A	D		P	A	R	S	L	E	Y		L	A	N	D

19 Letter Logic

D	O	V	E		C	U	R	R	A	N	T		S	A	N	D
	L		X		A		I		G		W		A		U	
M	I	N	T		V	I	P	E	R		O	X	F	O	R	D
	V		R		I		E		E				F		S	
R	E	M	O	V	A	L		R	E	D	C	A	R	P	E	T
			V		R		R				O		O			
C	O	M	E	T		F	A	C	T	O	R		N	E	A	T
	P		R		S		D		I		N				D	
H	E	A	T		P	L	I	N	T	H		B	R	A	V	E
	R				O		A		A		W		E		A	
M	A	S	T	E	R		T	I	N		A	C	C	E	N	T
			E		T		O				T		Y		C	
A	P	E	X		S	U	R	N	A	M	E		C	H	E	F
	E		T		C				L		R		L			
A	R	N	I	C	A		Y	A	P		S	L	E	D	G	E
	G		L		R		I		H		H				L	
T	O	K	E	N		D	E	C	A	D	E		P	E	A	R
	L				A		L		B		D		R		S	
C	A	R	T		L	A	D	D	E	R		H	O	U	S	E
			R		O				T		C		G			
M	A	N	I	F	E	S	T	O		G	R	E	N	A	D	E
	L		B				O		I		A		O		U	
L	I	Q	U	O	R		M	O	N	E	Y		S	A	V	E
	E		N		I		E		T		O		I		E	
K	N	E	E		B	A	S	S	O	O	N		S	A	T	E

20 Letter Logic

T	O	A	D		P	R	O	V	E	R	B		S	I	L	K
	M		A		I		V		N		I		H		A	
E	B	O	N		G	U	E	S	T		L	E	A	N	T	O
	R		G		L		N		E		B		L		I	
L	E	V	E	R	E	T		G	R	E	E	N	L	A	N	D
			R		T		L				R		O			
P	I	L	O	T		S	I	M	M	E	R		T	A	S	K
	N		U		S		F		O		Y				T	
O	D	D	S		T	R	E	M	O	R		B	A	K	E	R
	I				A		B		S		R		R		A	
T	A	I	L	O	R		O	D	E		E	N	C	A	M	P
			A		G		A				B		H		E	
F	A	C	T		A	R	T	I	S	T	E		W	A	R	M
	P		T		Z				H		L		A			
M	O	B	I	L	E		L	E	O		L	A	Y	O	U	T
	S		C		R		U		U		I				N	
S	T	E	E	L		A	P	O	L	L	O		A	C	I	D
	L				E		I		D		N		T		O	
M	E	S	S		C	A	N	T	E	R		C	H	A	N	T
			H		L				R		W		L			
M	A	N	I	F	E	S	T	O		F	R	I	E	N	D	S
	R		N		C		A		A		I		T		R	
N	O	U	G	A	T		R	I	G	H	T		I	R	A	N
	M		L		I		O		R		H		C		M	
B	A	L	E		C	O	T	T	A	G	E		S	N	A	P

1 Codewords

	S		A		W		B		D		L	
O	P	A	Q	U	E		E	Y	E	L	E	T
	H		U		T		R		M		T	
V	I	S	A		S	K	Y	L	I	G	H	T
	N				U		L		J		A	
E	X	C	L	A	I	M		D	O	L	L	Y
			I		T		R		H			
S	T	A	F	F		R	E	E	N	T	R	Y
	R		E		B		A				E	
N	E	W	S	R	E	E	L		L	O	V	E
	B		I		R		I		O		I	
B	L	A	Z	E	R		S	H	A	K	E	R
	E		E		Y		M		N		W	

2 Codewords

	E		I		S		A		M		O	
O	X	Y	G	E	N		S	C	U	R	V	Y
	A		N		U		P		Z		E	
A	M	M	O		B	L	I	Z	Z	A	R	D
			R		B		C		L		K	
S	W	E	E	T	E	N		R	E	J	I	G
	A				R		D				L	
S	T	A	C	K		M	I	S	S	I	L	E
	C		A		E		L		U			
P	H	Y	S	I	Q	U	E		B	A	R	K
	F		I		U		M		W		O	
G	U	I	N	E	A		M	E	A	D	O	W
	L		O		L		A		Y		F	

3 Codewords

L	A	T	E		B	O	O	K	S	H	O	P
A		E		S		D		U		E		I
S	E	A	F	O	O	D		M	I	X	U	P
T		R		F		I		Q		A		E
P	A	S	T	A		T	R	U	D	G	E	
O						Y		A		O		C
S	I	T	U	P	S		S	T	A	N	Z	A
T		E		O		L						S
	C	L	O	T	H	O		T	O	R	C	H
P		A		H		G		A		A		F
L	E	V	E	E		J	O	U	R	N	A	L
O		I		R		A		T		C		O
D	I	V	E	B	O	M	B		C	H	E	W

4 Codewords

G	L	A	M	O	U	R		B	A	T	C	H
L		R		V		O		U		A		Y
E	X	C	H	E	Q	U	E	R		B	A	G
B				R		T		S		L		I
E	M	B	E	D		E	X	T	R	E	M	E
		L		U		S				W		N
E	N	A	M	E	L		E	S	C	A	P	E
X		C				S		A		R		
P	I	K	E	L	E	T		T	R	E	S	S
L		J		A		U		S				C
A	G	A		I	N	F	L	U	E	N	Z	A
I		C		R		F		M		U		L
N	A	K	E	D		Y	E	A	R	N	E	D

5 Codewords

J	U	T	E		F	L	A	G	S	H	I	P
U		A		A		U		R		A		A
N	E	S	T	B	O	X		O	R	D	E	R
K		T		S		U		A		D		K
M	A	Y	B	E		R	A	N	D	O	M	
A				I		Y				C		S
I	N	S	U	L	T		H	A	C	K	L	E
L		Q				B		R				A
	R	U	S	S	I	A		C	H	A	O	S
D		E		C		M		A		W		H
O	P	E	R	A		B	A	N	D	A	G	E
D		Z		R		O		E		K		L
O	V	E	R	F	L	O	W		B	E	L	L

6 Codewords

	M		S		S		S		M		F	
H	I	J	A	C	K		I	T	A	L	I	C
	C		L		Y		N		R		G	
G	A	L	A		B	O	U	T	I	Q	U	E
			M		L		S		N		R	
O	M	N	I	B	U	S		B	A	S	I	L
	A				E		S				N	
C	R	E	E	K		G	U	M	T	R	E	E
	Z		L		E		G		I			
M	I	X	E	D	B	A	G		N	A	V	Y
	P		V		O		E		D		I	
C	A	V	E	R	N		S	W	E	R	V	E
	N		N		Y		T		R		A	

7 Codewords

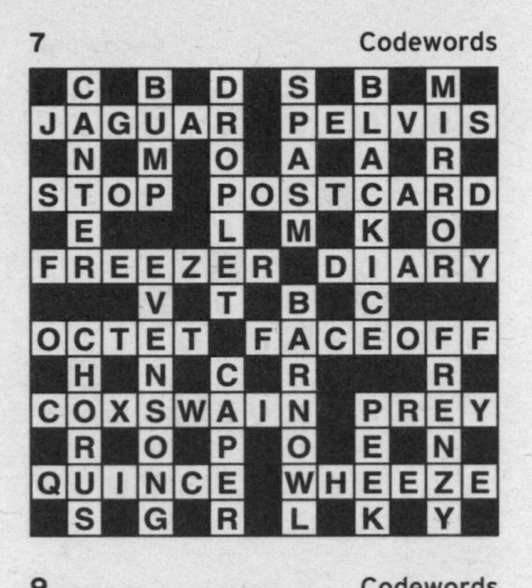

	C		B		D		S		B		M	
J	A	G	U	A	R		P	E	L	V	I	S
	N		M		O		A		A		R	
S	T	O	P		P	O	S	T	C	A	R	D
	E				L		M		K		O	
F	R	E	E	Z	E	R		D	I	A	R	Y
			V		T		B		C			
O	C	T	E	T		F	A	C	E	O	F	F
	H		N		C		R				R	
C	O	X	S	W	A	I	N		P	R	E	Y
	R		O		P		O		E		N	
Q	U	I	N	C	E		W	H	E	E	Z	E
	S		G		R		L		K		Y	

8 Codewords

F	O	N	D	A	N	T		K	N	E	L	L
A		E		C		H		H		X		A
B	A	R	O	Q	U	E		A	S	P	E	N
L		V		U		O		K		L		T
E	L	E	M	I		R	H	I	Z	O	M	E
				R		Y				R		R
C	O	P	P	E	R		S	P	L	E	E	N
H		R				O		E				
A	D	E	N	O	I	D		N	A	M	E	S
S		V		T		D		G		A		T
S	A	I	N	T		J	O	U	R	N	E	Y
I		E		E		O		I		I		L
S	E	W	E	R		B	A	N	D	A	G	E

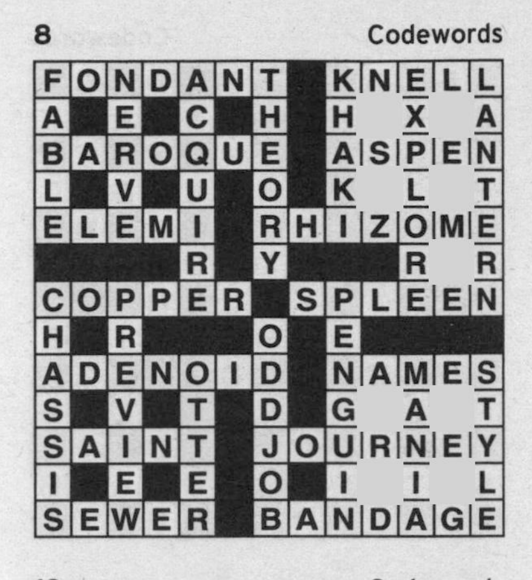

9 Codewords

H	O	T	E	L		B	E	L	L	J	A	R
O		E		A		O		Y		A		O
M	A	N	X	C	A	T		R	O	Y	A	L
E		O		Q		A		I		W		L
B	A	N	T	U		N	E	C	T	A	R	
R				E		Y				L		E
E	M	P	I	R	E		B	A	S	K	E	T
W		R				T		V				H
	C	O	S	T	A	R		E	M	P	T	Y
B		D		A		I		R		I		L
A	L	I	E	N		F	R	A	Z	Z	L	E
C		G		G		L		G		Z		N
K	E	Y	N	O	T	E		E	V	A	D	E

10 Codewords

Q	U	I	Z		C	R	O	S	S	I	N	G
U		R		C		H		M		C		A
A	V	O	C	A	D	O		A	L	E	R	T
N		N		M		D		R		B		E
T	H	Y	M	E		E	N	T	R	E	E	
I				R		S				R		T
T	O	P	H	A	T		K	U	N	G	F	U
Y		I				T		N				G
	G	L	I	D	E	R		L	I	M	B	O
G		L		I		O		O		I		F
O	R	B	I	T		J	A	C	K	D	A	W
L		O		T		A		K		G		A
F	O	X	H	O	U	N	D		B	E	A	R

11 Codewords

C	O	N	Q	U	E	R		C	O	A	C	H
A		Y		P		A		O		I		E
D	E	L	I	G	H	T		B	O	R	A	X
E		O		R		T		R		L		A
T	O	N	G	A		A	M	A	Z	I	N	G
				D		N				F		O
H	E	A	L	E	R		C	A	R	T	O	N
A		N				S		D				
T	R	A	N	S	I	T		J	E	W	E	L
C		G		H		R		U		O		I
H	O	R	S	E		U	N	N	E	R	V	E
E		A		E		C		C		T		I
T	I	M	E	R		K	I	T	C	H	E	N

12 Codewords

H	U	G	E		I	B	I	S		M	A	P
I		R		A		O		E		I		A
G	E	A	R	B	O	X		R	A	D	O	N
H		I		L		C		G		W		G
J	U	N	T	A		A	B	E	L	I	A	
U				Z		R				F		Q
M	O	C	K	E	R		G	A	T	E	A	U
P		O				D		L				E
	B	O	B	B	L	E		C	L	A	S	S
A		K		L		G		O		R		T
C	R	E	P	E		R	A	V	I	O	L	I
I		R		S		E		E		M		O
D	A	Y		S	T	E	W		B	A	R	N

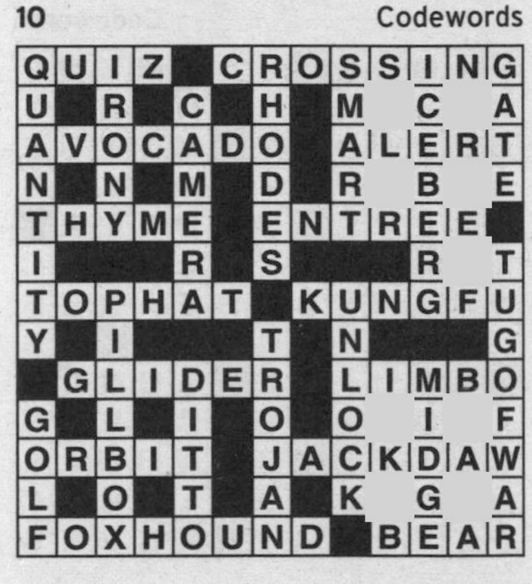

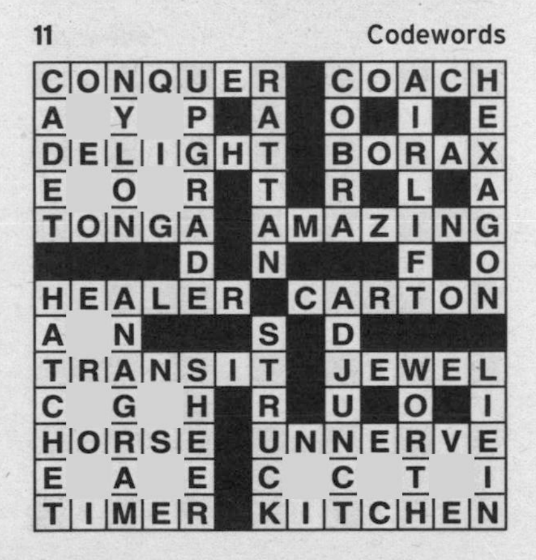

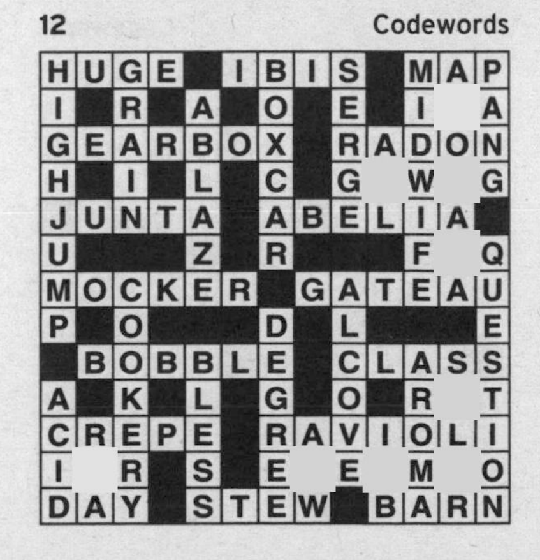

13 Codewords

	E		O		N		E		F		C	
J	U	M	B	L	E		A	N	O	R	A	K
	R		O		T		R		X		J	
F	E	T	E		W	A	T	C	H	D	O	G
	K				O		H		O		L	
V	A	M	P	I	R	E		D	U	V	E	T
			I		K		C		N			
B	A	I	Z	E		S	O	L	D	I	E	R
	B		Z		C		O				Q	
F	R	E	E	K	I	C	K		B	L	U	E
	O		R		D		E		E		I	
S	A	T	I	R	E		R	E	L	A	T	E
	D		A		R		Y		T		Y	

14 Codewords

	H		F		A		O		C		G	
Q	U	A	R	T	Z		V	I	O	L	E	T
	L		E		I		U		B		N	
P	A	S	S		M	I	L	K	W	E	E	D
			C		U		E		E		R	
E	F	F	O	R	T	S		U	B	O	A	T
	O				H		B				T	
O	X	B	O	W		B	O	O	T	L	E	G
	G		R		C		X		I			
F	L	A	P	J	A	C	K		C	O	P	Y
	O		H		L		I		K		L	
A	V	I	A	R	Y		T	R	E	M	O	R
	E		N		X		E		T		D	

15 Codewords

P	I	Q	U	E		J	A	S	M	I	N	E
U		U		N		O		N		N		V
B	L	O	W	D	R	Y		A	N	K	L	E
C		T		U		F		F		L		N
R	E	E	V	E		U	N	F	A	I	R	
A						L		L		N		N
W	H	A	R	F	S		B	E	A	G	L	E
L		P		R		R						U
	S	P	L	I	C	E		S	U	G	A	R
A		O		Z		S		C		L		O
B	L	I	T	Z		C	H	A	M	O	I	S
L		N		L		U		L		B		I
E	X	T	R	E	M	E		P	R	E	S	S

16 Codewords

J	A	C	O	B	I	N		R	O	A	C	H
U		A		A		Y		E		I		A
I	L	L	E	G	A	L		L	Y	R	I	C
C		V		H		O		A		P		K
Y	I	E	L	D		N	O	X	I	O	U	S
				A		S				R		A
D	E	C	A	D	E		B	E	S	T	O	W
E		Y				I		Q				
P	H	A	N	T	O	M		U	M	B	E	R
O		N		R		P		A		R		E
S	H	I	N	E		O	U	T	S	I	Z	E
I		D		A		R		O		E		D
T	H	E	F	T		T	H	R	I	F	T	Y

17 Codewords

C	U	L	V	E	R	T		B	A	D	G	E
O		A		X		U		A		E		V
W	H	I	M	P	E	R		C	R	A	Z	E
O		R		L		T		O		D		N
R	O	D	E	O		L	I	N	N	E	T	
K				I		E				N		G
E	I	G	H	T	Y		A	C	A	D	I	A
R		R				U		A				R
	A	I	R	M	A	N		S	H	R	U	G
A		Z		A		I		C		A		O
J	A	Z	Z	Y		Q	U	A	L	I	F	Y
A		L		B		U		D		S		L
R	H	Y	M	E		E	X	E	G	E	T	E

18 Codewords

	G		B		S		S		S		K	
G	A	L	A	X	Y		C	R	E	D	I	T
	L		L		M		R		Q		N	
N	A	I	L		P	R	E	J	U	D	G	E
			E		T		E		I		C	
E	M	O	T	I	O	N		A	N	G	R	Y
	A				M		P				A	
B	R	A	S	S		W	A	L	L	A	B	Y
	Z		P		C		S		O			
V	I	G	I	L	A	N	T		O	K	R	A
	P		R		M		U		F		O	
M	A	R	I	N	E		R	E	A	S	O	N
	N		T		E		E		H		K	

19 Codewords

	M		A		W		P		H		R	
Q	U	I	C	H	E		R	E	A	D	E	R
	S		I		D		O		L		G	
U	S	E	D		D	O	X	O	L	O	G	Y
	E				I		Y		M		A	
E	L	E	G	A	N	T		B	A	K	E	R
			O		G		M		R			
B	E	L	L	Y		B	A	C	K	L	O	G
	L		F		E		G				D	
Z	I	M	B	A	B	W	E		C	O	D	E
	X		A		O		N		H		J	
V	I	O	L	I	N		T	E	A	P	O	T
	R		L		Y		A		P		B	

20 Codewords

S	H	A	C	K	L	E		J	U	D	A	S
E		R		N		S		I		R		K
D	R	O	P	O	U	T		G	R	I	M	Y
G		M		W		O		G		Z		B
E	M	A	I	L		P	R	E	T	Z	E	L
				E				R		L		U
E	L	F		D	A	I	L	Y		E	V	E
X		L		G				P				
C	L	E	M	E	N	T		O	R	B	I	T
U		X		A		I		K		L		W
S	Q	U	I	B		E	L	E	V	A	T	E
E		R		L		U		R		D		E
S	U	E	D	E		P	A	Y	M	E	N	T

1 Crossword

	G		T		A		S		A		H	
C	A	Y	E	N	N	E	P	E	P	P	E	R
	R		E		D		U		O		L	
A	B	A	T	T	O	I	R		G	A	L	L
			E		V		N		E		B	
S	C	A	R	P	E	R		B	E	R	E	T
	O				R		F				N	
B	L	I	M	P		M	A	M	M	O	T	H
	L		A		S		L		U			
L	O	U	R		C	O	L	O	S	S	A	L
	Q		G		R		A		C		F	
M	U	S	I	C	A	L	C	H	A	I	R	S
	Y		N		G		Y		T		O	

2 Crossword

3 Crossword

	A		K		K		M		H		R	
R	E	G	A	L	E		E	X	E	T	E	R
	R		L		S		R		S		L	
B	A	S	E		T	E	R	M	I	N	A	L
	T				R		Y		T		T	
D	E	L	I	V	E	R		E	A	G	E	R
			N		L		D		T			
G	U	S	T	O		D	I	L	E	M	M	A
	P		R		D		V				O	
G	R	U	E	S	O	M	E		C	U	R	T
	O		P		N		R		O		S	
H	A	L	I	T	E		S	A	L	V	E	R
	R		D		E		E		A		L	

4 Crossword

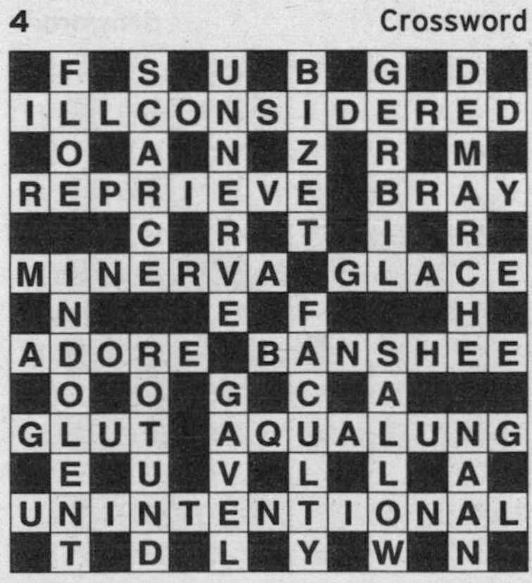

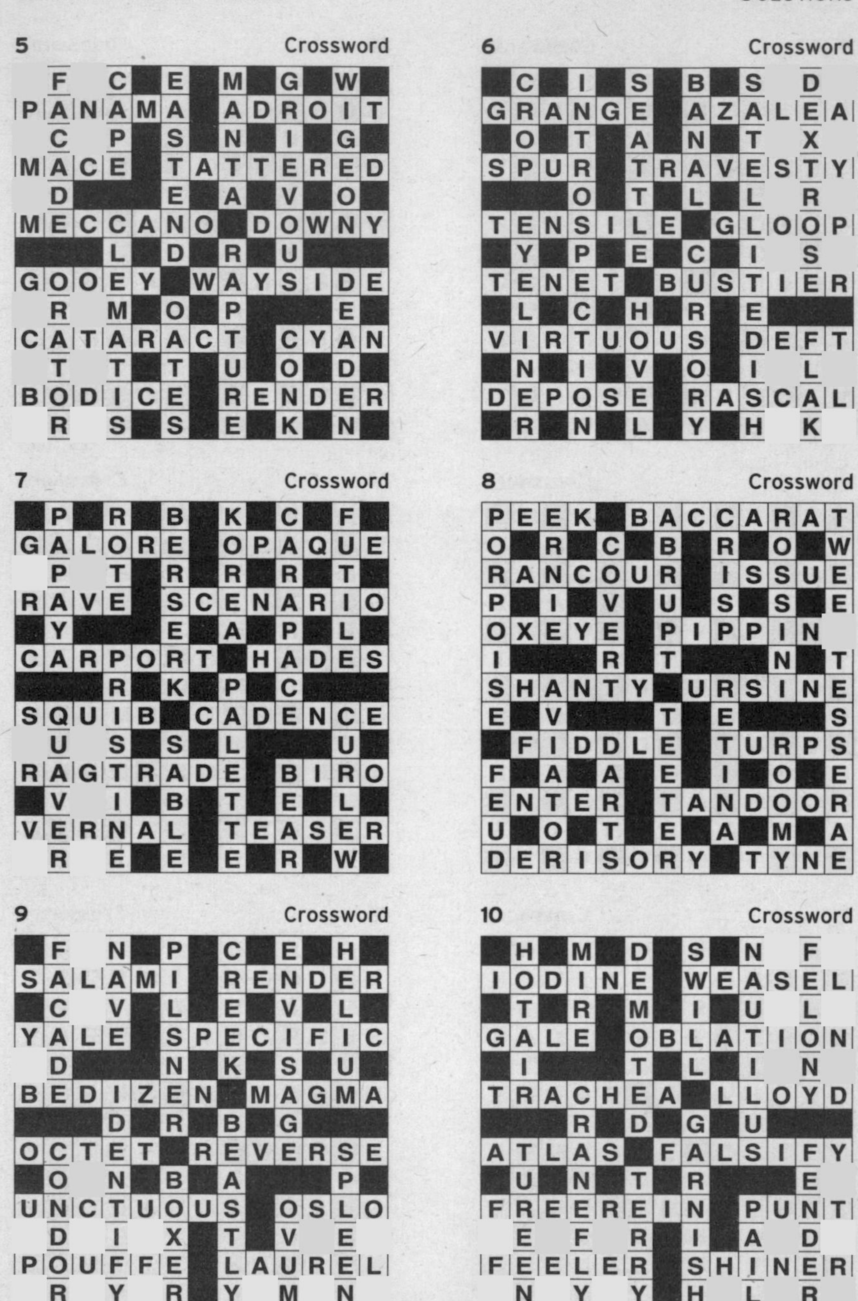

11 Crossword

C	A	S	K		C	A	L	C	U	L	U	S
O		N		C		S		U		E		M
C	H	A	M	O	I	S		R	A	N	G	E
K		R		C		E		I		I		E
S	N	E	A	K		S	H	O	V	E	L	
U				L		S				N		D
R	O	T	T	E	R		G	R	O	T	T	O
E		E				L		A				W
	P	R	I	C	E	Y		P	R	A	W	N
O		M		R		R		T		W		B
G	R	I	P	E		I	R	O	N	A	G	E
R		T		E		C		R		S		A
E	Y	E	G	L	A	S	S		W	H	I	T

12 Crossword

	T		T		D		J		C		T	
B	O	R	A	G	E		A	P	A	T	H	Y
	B		U		C		M		R		A	
W	A	R	T		L	A	M	B	A	S	T	E
	G				I		Y		P		C	
R	O	S	S	I	N	I		B	A	T	H	E
			K		E		P		C			
H	E	L	E	N		S	E	N	E	G	A	L
	X		L		H		R				V	
F	O	R	E	C	A	S	T		O	B	O	E
	D		T		S		U		P		C	
A	U	F	A	I	T		R	E	E	F	E	R
	S		L		Y		B		N		T	

13 Crossword

	G		M		S		C		B		I	
B	L	O	O	D	C	U	R	D	L	I	N	G
	E		R		U		O		I		F	
T	E	R	R	A	P	I	N		T	R	E	K
			I		P		Y		H		R	
L	E	I	S	T	E	R		G	E	L	I	D
	L				R		G				O	
D	E	C	R	Y		C	U	R	S	O	R	Y
	V		E		W		B		P			
L	A	O	S		A	R	B	O	R	E	A	L
	T		I		G		I		I		N	
C	O	N	S	T	E	R	N	A	T	I	O	N
	R		T		R		S		E		N	

14 Crossword

S	H	I	N		P	E	N	C	H	A	N	T
L		D		R		G		O		I		E
A	M	A	T	E	U	R		R	U	M	B	A
P		H		V		E		A		L		K
D	R	O	N	E		S	I	L	V	E	R	
A				R		S				S		R
S	O	C	C	E	R		P	U	R	S	U	E
H		L				U		N				H
	G	A	T	H	E	R		E	M	C	E	E
A		V		Y		B		V		H		A
C	H	I	D	E		A	T	E	L	I	E	R
I		E		N		N		N		N		S
D	A	R	K	A	G	E	S		J	O	V	E

15 Crossword

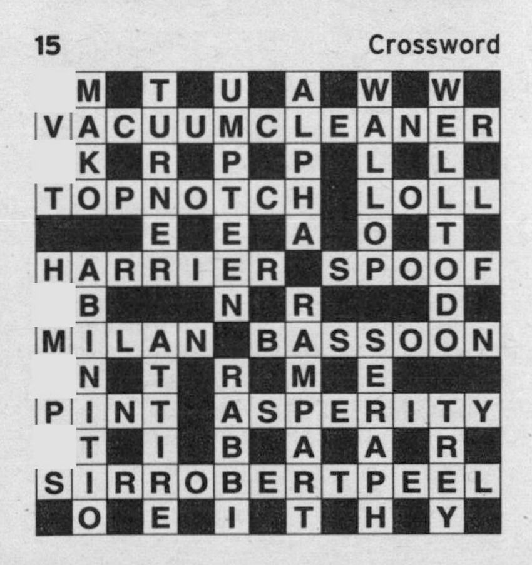

	M		T		U		A		W		W	
V	A	C	U	U	M	C	L	E	A	N	E	R
	K		R		P		P		L		L	
T	O	P	N	O	T	C	H		L	O	L	L
			E		E		A		O		T	
H	A	R	R	I	E	R		S	P	O	O	F
	B				N		R				D	
M	I	L	A	N		B	A	S	S	O	O	N
	N		T		R		M		E			
P	I	N	T		A	S	P	E	R	I	T	Y
	T		I		B		A		A		R	
S	I	R	R	O	B	E	R	T	P	E	E	L
	O		E		I		T		H		Y	

16 Crossword

M	U	S	H		C	A	L	C	U	T	T	A
A		C		D		R		A		O		C
R	H	O	D	I	U	M		B	Y	R	O	N
K		R		N		A		L		R		E
S	T	E	R	N		D	E	E	M	E	D	
M				E		A				N		D
A	B	S	O	R	B		M	A	N	T	L	E
N		P				M		S				R
	T	A	T	T	L	E		T	U	T	O	R
L		N		O		T		R		E		I
O	R	I	O	N		T	E	A	T	R	E	E
G		E		D		L		L		S		R
O	N	L	O	O	K	E	R		G	E	N	E

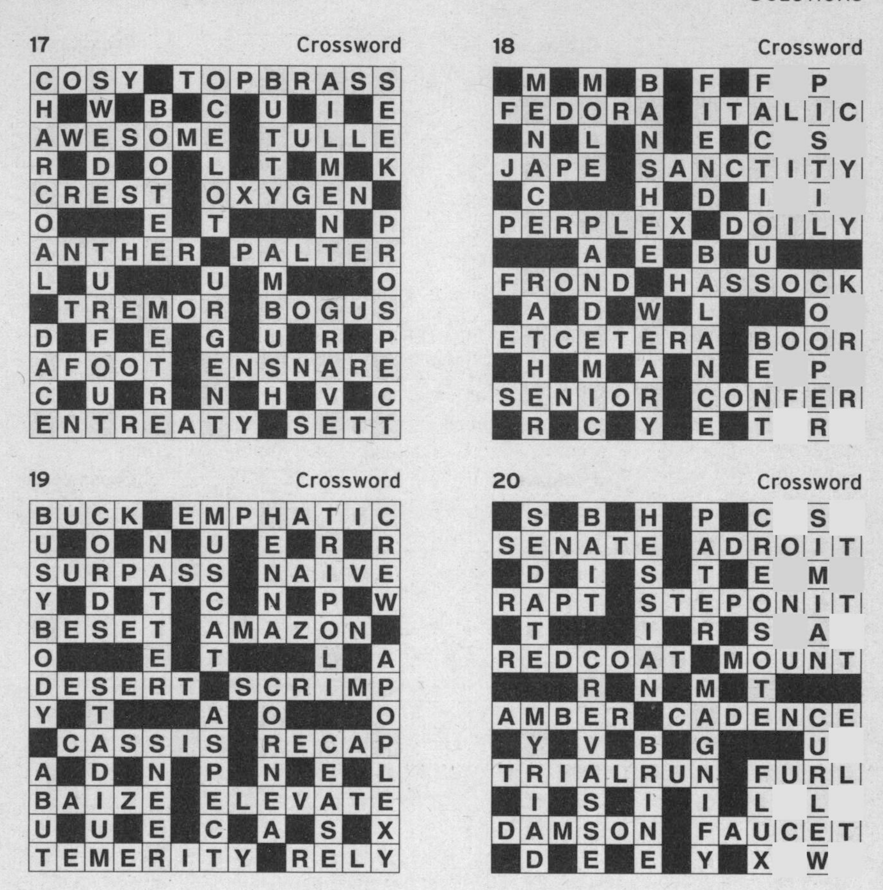

1 Pathfinder

CUPCAKE, JAM TART, BATTENBURG, CHOCOLATE BROWNIE, BLACK FOREST GATEAU, CINNAMON SWIRL, BAKEWELL TART, FUDGE CAKE, VICTORIA SANDWICH, MACAROON, BATH BUN, TREACLE TART, PARKIN, SACHERTORTE, MADELEINE, PETIT FOUR, BRIOCHE, RUM BABA, BAKLAVA, STOLLEN, TEACAKE, FLAPJACK, CREAM PUFF, SCONE

2 Pathfinder

BRIGHTON ROCK, BROTHERS IN LAW, DUNKIRK, THE LEAGUE OF GENTLEMEN, THE ANGRY SILENCE, THE GREAT ESCAPE, DOCTOR DOLITTLE, ONLY WHEN I LARF, AND THEN THERE WERE NONE, JURASSIC PARK, ELIZABETH, THE RAILWAY CHILDREN, A BRIDGE TOO FAR, GANDHI, A CHORUS LINE, CRY FREEDOM, CHAPLIN, SHADOWLANDS

3 **Pathfinder**

BULLDOG, HUSKY, SPANIEL, PINSCHER, BEAGLE, COLLIE, BICHON FRISE, BOXER, SHEEPDOG, CHIHUAHUA, DACHSHUND, DALMATIAN, DOBERMAN, SCHNAUZER, GREYHOUND, JACK RUSSELL, LURCHER, NEWFOUNDLAND, PAPILLON, PEKINESE, POMERANIAN, GERMAN SHEPHERD, POODLE, ROTTWEILER, RED SETTER, MASTIFF, WHIPPET

4 **Pathfinder**

AS YOU LIKE IT, THE MERCHANT OF VENICE, A MIDSUMMER NIGHTS DREAM, MUCH ADO ABOUT NOTHING, ROMEO AND JULIET, CORIOLANUS, JULIUS CAESAR, KING LEAR, ANTONY AND CLEOPATRA, THE WINTERS TALE, CYMBELINE, VENUS AND ADONIS, MEASURE FOR MEASURE, THE TAMING OF THE SHREW, ALLS WELL THAT ENDS WELL

5 **Pathfinder**

WAFFLE IRON, CHOPPING BOARD, STEAMER, EGG TIMER, PESTLE AND, MORTAR, BAIN MARIE, SKILLET, GARLIC PRESS, PEPPER MILL, MEAT THERMOMETER, ROLLING PIN, WOODEN SPOON, TONGS, MIXING BOWL, BLENDER, SPATULA, BREAD KNIFE, FRYING PAN, WHISK, CHEESE GRATER, TIN OPENER, STRAINER, COLANDER, MANDOLINE

6 **Pathfinder**

EASTINDIA, WIMBLEDON, BERMONDSEY, RUSSELL SQUARE, HAMPSTEAD, MORNINGTON CRESCENT, BAKER STREET, OXFORD CIRCUS, WESTMINSTER, PADDINGTON, PUTNEY BRIDGE, FARRINGDON, ACTON TOWN, ROTHERHITHE, BANK, ST JOHNS WOOD, SWISS COTTAGE, UXBRIDGE, WEMBLEY CENTRAL COCKFOSTERS, CANARY WHARF

7 **Pathfinder**

ANCHOR, FATHOM, BULKHEAD, TAKENABACK, STARBOARD, BRIDGE, CHASEGUNS, CLEWLINE, DOGWATCH, PORT, HAMMOCK, KEEL, LEAGUE, MIZZENSTAYSAIL, DECKHAND, BINNACLE, SCUPPERS, PREVENTER, TOPGALLENT, GALLEY, WHEELHOUSE, YARDARM, BOWLINE, BRIDGE, COXSWAIN, LEEWARD, SPINNAKER, MIDSHIPMAN, SKIPPER

8 **Pathfinder**

MARS, ASTEROID, JUPITER, APOLLO, TITAN, VENUS, MOON, METEOR, NEPTUNE, PLUTO, CERES, HALLEYS COMET, ECLIPSE, PERIHELION, ORBITAL, GRAVITY, SPACESTATION, TELESCOPE, HUBBLE, GALAXY, OORTCLOUD, GANYMEDE, SATURN, URANUS, SHUTTLE, HOUSTON, SPUTNIK, ASTRONAUT, BLACKHOLE, CONSTELLATION, NEBULA

---

9 **Pathfinder**

GUITAR, OBOE, BASSOON, FLUTE, DIDGERIDOO, OCARINA, PANPIPES, TIN WHISTLE, PICCOLO, CLARINET, SAXOPHONE, TROMBONE, BUGLE, FRENCH HORN, TUBA, HARMONICA, BANJO, CELLO, DOUBLE BASS, HARP, HURDY GURDY, MANDOLIN, PIANO, SITAR, TRUMPET, VIOLIN, CYMBAL, GLOCKENSPIEL, TRIANGLE, SYNTHESIZER, CORNET

---

10 **Pathfinder**

HARVEY WALLBANGER, MARTINI, MANHATTAN, BLACK RUSSIAN, SANGRIA,GIN SLING, BRANDY ALEXANDER, SNOWBALL, SINGAPORE SLING, MOSCOW MULE, BLOODY MARY, SIDECAR, LONG ISLAND ICED TEA, TOM COLLINS, BACARDI, TEQUILA SLAMMER, COSMOPOLITAN, SCREWDRIVER, SEX ON THE BEACH, KIR ROYALE, AMERICANO

---

11 **Pathfinder**

GREENLAND, NEW GUINEA, BORNEO, MADAGASCAR, BAFFIN ISLAND, SUMATRA, HONSHU, GREAT BRITAIN, VICTORIA ISLAND, ELLESMERE ISLAND, SOUTH ISLAND, JAVA, NORTH ISLAND, LUZON, NEWFOUNDLAND, CUBA, ICELAND, IRELAND, HOKKAIDO, HISPANIOLA, SAKHALIN, BANKS ISLAND, SRI LANKA, TASMANIA,DEVON ISLAND

---

12 **Pathfinder**

HYDROGEN, HELIUM, LITHIUM, BERYLLIUM, BORON, CARBON, NITROGEN, OXYGEN, FLUORINE, NEON, SODIUM, MAGNESIUM, ALUMINIUM, SILICON, PHOSPHORUS, CHLORINE, ARGON, POTASSIUM, CALCIUM, SCANDIUM, TITANIUM, VANADIUM, CHROMIUM, MANGANESE, IRON, COBALT, NICKEL, COPPER, ZINC, ARSENIC, BROMINE, KRYPTON

---

13 **Pathfinder**

COMMISION, BANKRUPTCY, BASE RATE, FISCAL YEAR, INSOLVENCY, REVENUE, INDEX LINKED, DEVALUATION, REDUNDANCY, INCOME TAX, EXCHANGE RATE, INVESTMENT, LIQUID ASSET, NATIONAL DEBT, PENSION FUND, BUDGET, TRADE UNION, STOCK BROKER, COMMODITY, SHAREHOLDER, SLUMP, PREMIUM BOND, UNDERWRITER

---

14 **Pathfinder**

PUMPKIN, MAUVE, ECRU, BURNT UMBER, CARDINAL, COBALT, AMETHYST, COPPER, DENIM, EMERALD, CERISE, AMBER, SAPPHIRE, HARLEQUIN, HOT PINK, CELADON, INDIGO, BRONZE, KHAKI, APRICOT, VERMILION, LINEN, MAGENTA, MOUNTBATTEN PINK, NAVAJO WHITE, OCHRE, AQUAMARINE, PERSIMMON, SAFFRON, BURGUNDY, CRIMSON

15 **Pathfinder**

RAYMOND BLANC, SOPHIE GRIGSON, JAMIE OLIVER, DELIA SMITH, ANTHONY WORRALL THOMPSON, ANTONIO CARLUCCIO, KEITH FLOYD, GARY RHODES, RICK STEIN, MARCO PIERRE WHITE, GORDON RAMSAY, JEAN CHRISTOPHE NOVELLLI, PRUE LEITH, MADHUR JAFFREY, KEN HOM, HUGH FEARNLEY WHITTINGSTALL, MRS BEETON

16 **Pathfinder**

DENMARK, TURKEY, HAITI, THAILAND, LIBYA, FRANCE, MALAYSIA, VIETNAM, JAPAN, INDIA, TUNISIA, ARGENTINA, URUGUAY, CHILE, POLAND, ALBANIA, ECUADOR, FINLAND, GERMANY, YEMEN, ICELAND, IRAQ, JAMAICA, RUSSIA, GREECE, NAMIBIA, PAKISTAN, BELGIUM, JERSEY, JORDAN, KENYA, UKRAINE, MALDIVES, NORWAY, SWEDEN

17 **Pathfinder**

HOT AIR BALLOON, MICROLIGHT, DOODLEBUG, AIRLINER, HUNTER, CONCORDE, BOMBER, GLIDER, BIPLANE, HELICOPTER, ZEPPELIN, AIRBUS, MESSERSCHMITT, HARRIER JUMP JET, DRONE, BLIMP, SEAPLANE, SPITFIRE, BOEING, LANCASTER, MONOPLANE, HERCULES, APACHE, SEAKING, LEARJET, NIMROD, HURRICANE, JUMBO JET

18 **Pathfinder**

BUGS BUNNY, HOMER SIMPSON, FRED FLINTSTONE, CHARLIE BROWN, SNOOPY, DAFFY DUCK, BETTY BOOP, TOPCAT, MICKEY MOUSE, POPEYE, SCOOBY DOO, WINNIE THE POOH, FELIX THE CAT, SYLVESTER, YOGI BEAR, MIGHTY MOUSE, WILE E COYOTE, ROADRUNNER, DONALD DUCK, WOODY WOODPECKER, PORKY PIG, TOM AND JERRY, GOOFY

19 **Pathfinder**

ALASKA, TEXAS, CALIFORNIA, MONTANA, NEW MEXICO, ARIZONA, NEVADA, COLORADO, WYOMING, OREGON, UTAH, MINNESOTA, KANSAS, NEBRASKA, OKLAHOMA, MISSOURI, WASHINGTON, GEORGIA, FLORIDA, MICHIGAN, ILLINOIS, IOWA, WISCONSIN, ARKANSAS, ALABAMA, NEW YORK, LOUISIANA, MISSISSIPPI, PENNSYLVANIA, OHIO,

20 **Pathfinder**

BLOOD IS THICKER THAN WATER, I THINK THEREFORE I AM, IGNORANCE IS BLISS, KNOWLEDGE IS POWER, ONE SWALLOW DOES NOT MAKE SUMMER, THE PEN IS MIGHTIER THAN THE SWORD, WE ARE NOT AMUSED, A WEEK IS A LONG TIME IN POLITICS, WONDERS WILL NEVER CEASE, RELIGION IS THE OPIUM OF THE PEOPLE, EUREKA!

1 Wordsearch

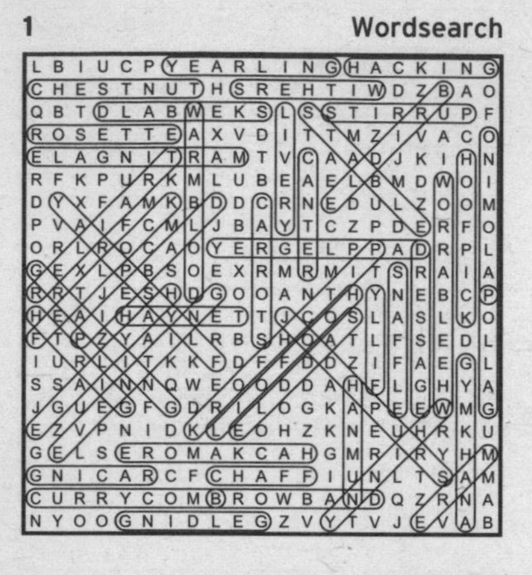

2 Wordsearch

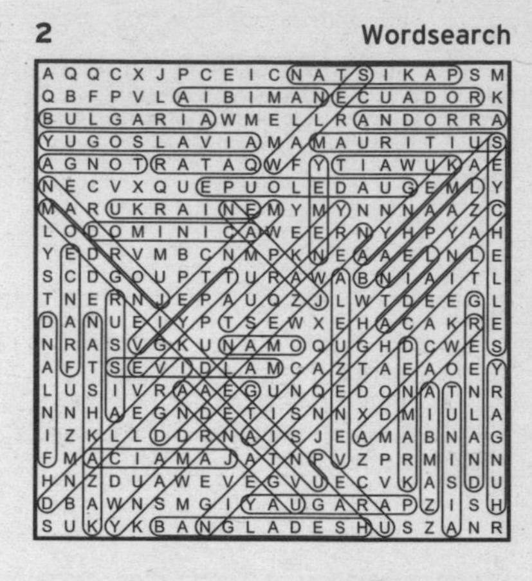

3 Wordsearch

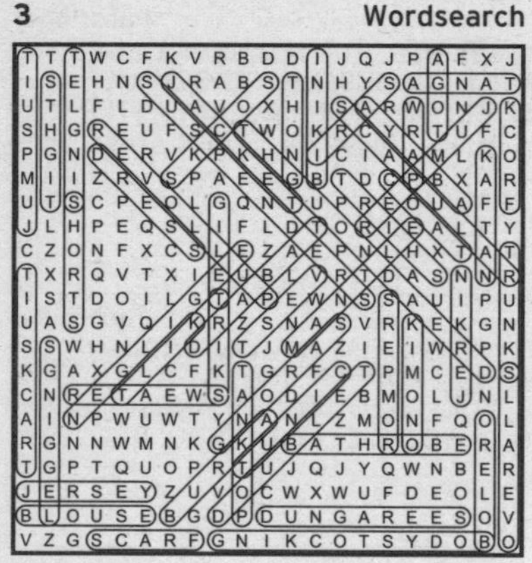

4 Wordsearch

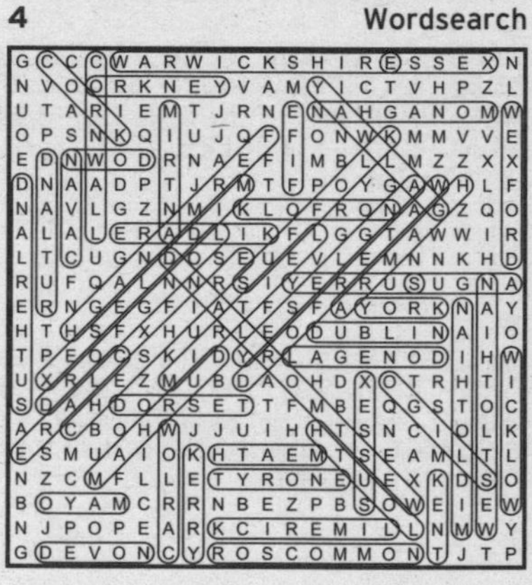

5 Wordsearch

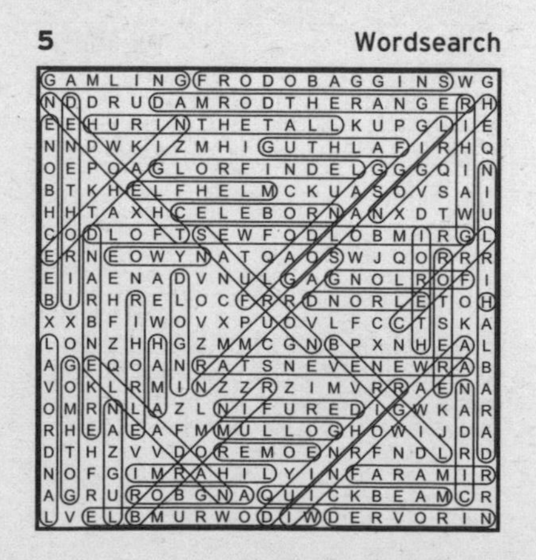

6 Wordsearch

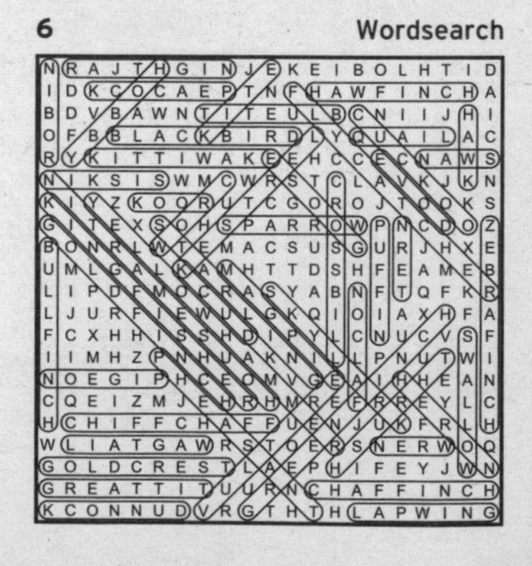

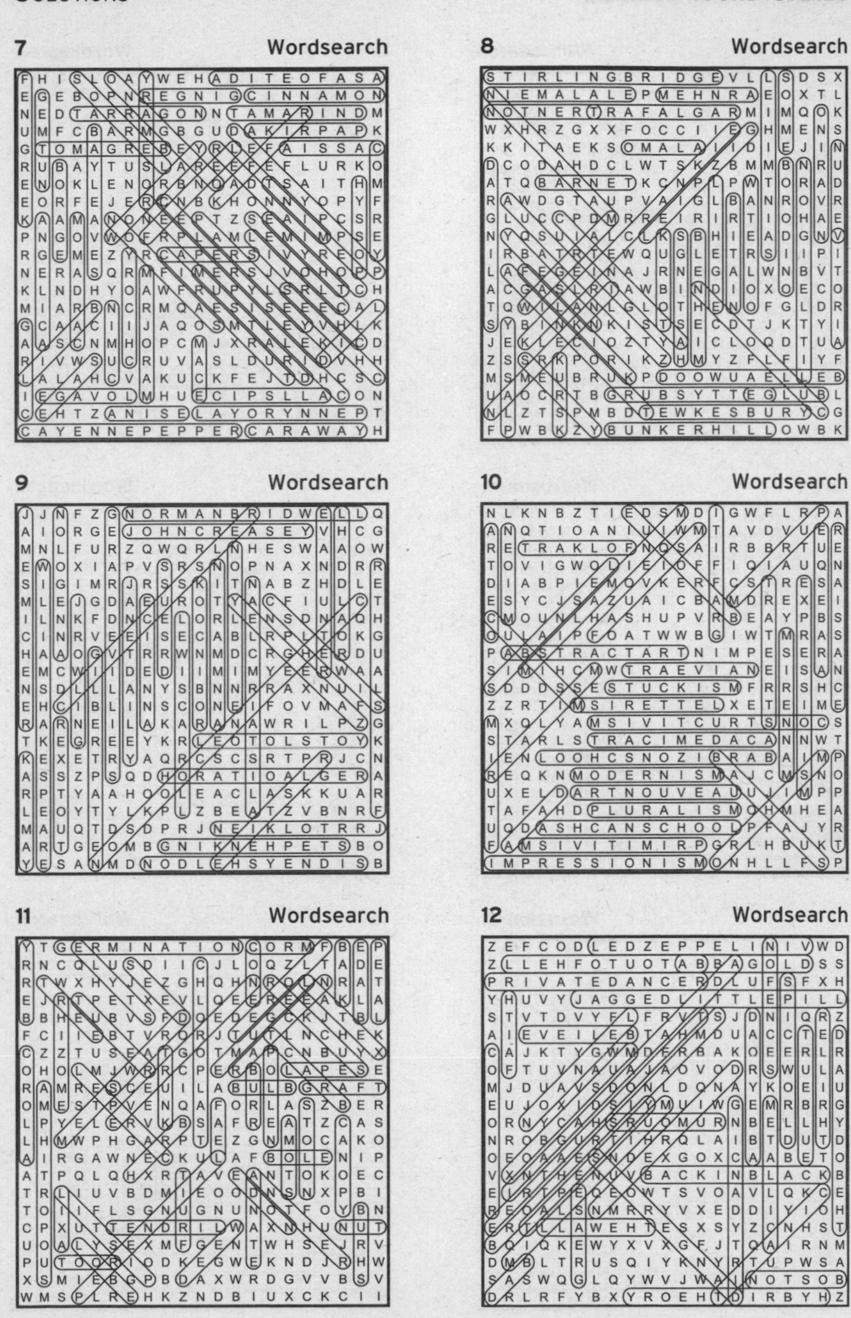

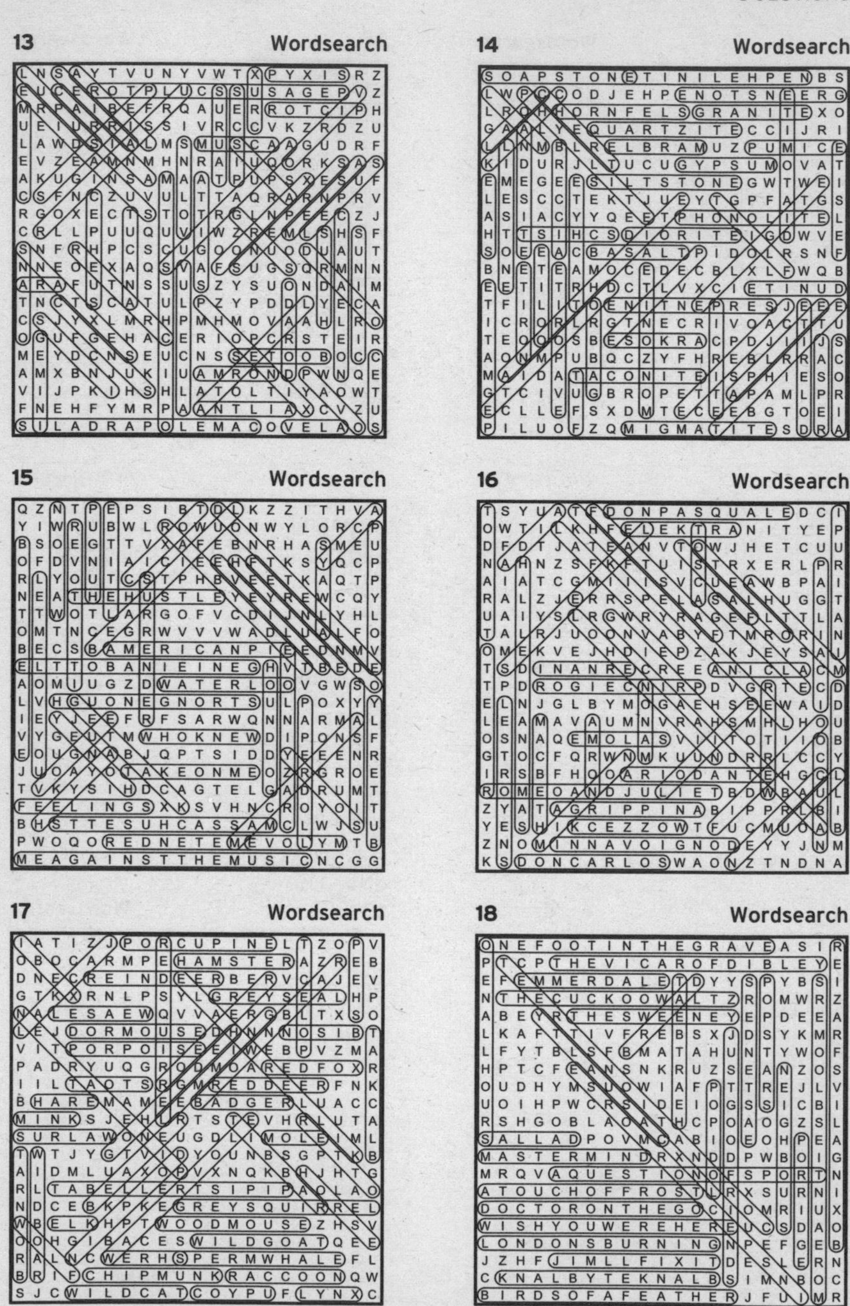
13 Wordsearch
14 Wordsearch
15 Wordsearch
16 Wordsearch
17 Wordsearch
18 Wordsearch

19 Wordsearch

20 Wordsearch

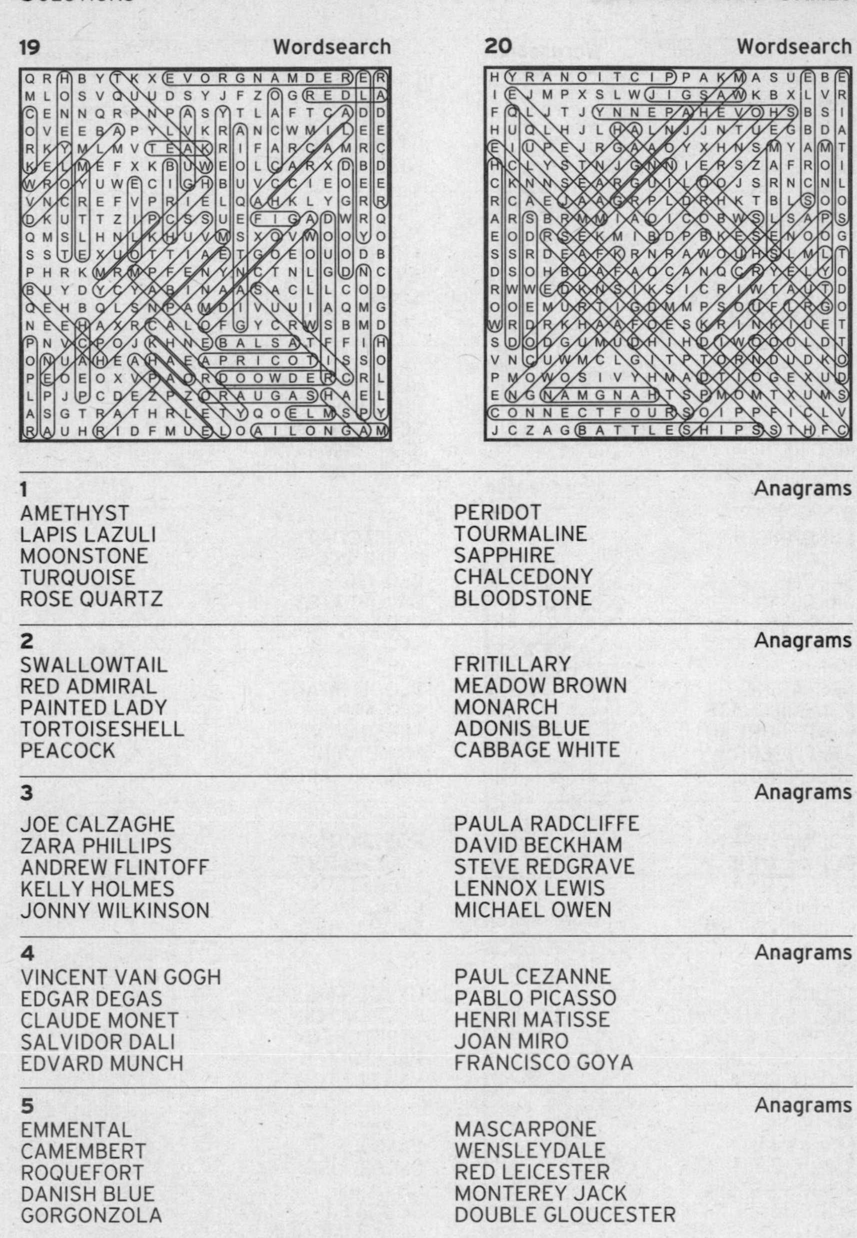

1 Anagrams

AMETHYST
LAPIS LAZULI
MOONSTONE
TURQUOISE
ROSE QUARTZ
PERIDOT
TOURMALINE
SAPPHIRE
CHALCEDONY
BLOODSTONE

2 Anagrams

SWALLOWTAIL
RED ADMIRAL
PAINTED LADY
TORTOISESHELL
PEACOCK
FRITILLARY
MEADOW BROWN
MONARCH
ADONIS BLUE
CABBAGE WHITE

3 Anagrams

JOE CALZAGHE
ZARA PHILLIPS
ANDREW FLINTOFF
KELLY HOLMES
JONNY WILKINSON
PAULA RADCLIFFE
DAVID BECKHAM
STEVE REDGRAVE
LENNOX LEWIS
MICHAEL OWEN

4 Anagrams

VINCENT VAN GOGH
EDGAR DEGAS
CLAUDE MONET
SALVIDOR DALI
EDVARD MUNCH
PAUL CEZANNE
PABLO PICASSO
HENRI MATISSE
JOAN MIRO
FRANCISCO GOYA

5 Anagrams

EMMENTAL
CAMEMBERT
ROQUEFORT
DANISH BLUE
GORGONZOLA
MASCARPONE
WENSLEYDALE
RED LEICESTER
MONTEREY JACK
DOUBLE GLOUCESTER

6 Anagrams

BADMINTON
WRESTLING
EQUESTRIAN
BOBSLEIGH
ICE HOCKEY
TABLE TENNIS
TAEKWONDO
TRIATHLON
GYMNASTICS
WEIGHTLIFTING

7 Anagrams

ROBERT PEEL
WILLIAM PITT
CLEMENT ATTLEE
HAROLD WILSON
EDWARD HEATH
TONY BLAIR
ANDREW BONAR LAW
ANTHONY EDEN
STANLEY BALDWIN
JAMES CALLAGHAN

8 Anagrams

TAWNY OWL
GOSHAWK
BALD EAGLE
KESTREL
MARSH HARRIER
VULTURE
BUZZARD
SCREECH OWL
SPARROWHAWK
SECRETARY BIRD

9 Anagrams

DUNGAREES
BODICE
SARONG
CARDIGAN
LEOTARD
WAISTCOAT
PASHMINA
BLOUSON
SALOPETTES
PEDAL PUSHERS

10 Anagrams

NECTARINE
POMEGRANATE
WHITE CURRANT
STRAWBERRY
GREENGAGE
BLOOD ORANGE
PINEAPPLE
PERSIMMON
MANDARIN
AVOCADO PEAR

11 Anagrams

BOLINGBROKE
CORIOLANUS
DESDEMONA
FERDINAND
GUILDENSTERN
ROSENCRANTZ
TOUCHSTONE
SEBASTIAN
DEMETRIUS
ENOBARBUS

12 Anagrams

TOURNIQUET
DIALYSIS MACHINE
DEFIBRILLATOR
STETHOSCOPE
MICROSCOPE
OXYGEN MASK
RESPIRATOR
STRETCHER
PACEMAKER
VENTILATOR

13 Anagrams

LEVIATHAN
SASQUATCH
FRANKENSTEIN
WEREWOLF
MINOTAUR
VAMPIRE
CERBERUS
CHIMERA
GODZILLA
COOKIE MONSTER

14 Anagrams

CAYENNE PEPPER
GARAM MASALA
CARAWAY SEED
LEMONGRASS
ASAFOETIDA
STAR ANISE
FENUGREEK
CHAMOMILE
BLACK PEPPER
CARDAMOM

15 Anagrams

PRAYING MANTIS
CRANE FLY
GRASSHOPPER
SPRINGTAIL
LEAFCUTTER ANT
COCKCHAFER
BLUEBOTTLE
DAMSELFLY
LEAFHOPPER
LACEWING

16 Anagrams

BLACKBURN ROVERS
BRISTOL CITY
CRYSTAL PALACE
DUNDEE UNITED
MIDDLESBROUGH
STENHOUSEMUIR
TRANMERE ROVERS
PORTSMOUTH
HIBERNIAN
LEYTON ORIENT

17 Anagrams

STAGE DIRECTION
FRONT OF HOUSE
LEADING LADY
UNDERSTUDY
STAGE FRIGHT
FIRST NIGHT
MONOLOGUE
BACKSTAGE
THESPIAN
CURTAIN CALL

18 Anagrams

STICKLEBACK
BROWN TROUT
MIRROR CARP
SWORDFISH
LEMON SOLE
BARRACUDA
MONK FISH
JOHN DORY
FLOUNDER
STURGEON

19 Anagrams

THE BEATLES
SHIRLEY BASSEY
LAURENCE OLIVIER
ALFRED HITCHCOCK
MAGGIE SMITH
TREVOR MCDONALD
CHRISTOPHER LEE
THE TWO RONNIES
MARGOT FONTEYN
TONY HANCOCK

20 Anagrams

AMONTILLADO
COTES DU RHONE
VERDICCHIO
ZINFANDEL
PINOT NOIR
CHARDONNAY
CHAMPAGNE
BEAUJOLAIS
MUSCADET
CORBIERES

1 **Polyword**

OBSTINACY, BOTANIC, TOCSIN, SCOTIA, SCANTY, NASTIC, CATION, CASINO, ATONIC, ACTION, TONIC, STOIC, SONIC, SCION, SCANT, ONTIC, COSTA, COBIA, COATI, COAST, CANTO, CANST, CABIN, BASIC, BANCO, BACON, ANTIC, ACTIN, TACO, SYNC, SOCA, SCOT, SCAT, SCAN, SCAB, OTIC, ICON, CYST, CYAN, COSY, COST, CONY, COIN, COAT, CITY, CIST, CIAO, CAST, CANT

2 **Polyword**

COLLEAGUE, ECLOGUE, COLLEGE, COLLAGE, ULLAGE, LOCULE, LOCALE, LEAGUE, COULEE, ALLEGE, LOCAL, LEGAL, GLACE, EAGLE, CELLO, CELLA, ALLEE, OGLE, LUGE, LUCE, LOGE, LEAL, LACE, GULL, GOAL, GLUE, GLEE, GAOL, GALL, GALE, CULL, COLE, COLA, COAL, CLUE, CLOG, CELL, CAUL, CALL, ALOE, ALEE

3 **Polyword**

PENSIONER, PENSIONE, ISOPRENE, PIONEER, PENSION, SOIREE, SENIOR, REPOSE, REOPEN, PRISON, PERSON, ORPINE, OPENER, NOSIER, SPORE, SNORE, SENOR, ROSIN, PROSE, PRONE, PRION, POSER, POISE, PINON, OSIER, ORPIN, OPINE, NONES, NOISE, EOSIN, SORE, SONE, ROSE, ROPE, REPO, POSE, PORN, PORE, PONS, PONE, PION, PESO, PEON, OPEN, NOSE, NORI, NOPE, NONE, NOIR, NEON, IRON, INRO

4 **Polyword**

ACCORDING, DRACONIC, ADORING, RANCID, ORDAIN, INROAD, GRADIN, GANOID, DRAGON, DARING, CODING, ACCORD, RADON, RADIO, NADIR, GRIND, GRAND, GONAD, DRAIN, DONGA, DOING, DINGO, DINAR, DANIO, CANID, AROID, ADORN, ACRID, ROAD, RIND, RAND, RAID, NARD, GRID, GRAD, GOAD, GIRD, DRAG, DONG, DING, DARN, DANG, DAGO, CORD, CODA, CARD, CADI, ARID, ACID

5 **Polyword**

OCCULTIST, OCULIST, CULTIST, STUCCO, OUTSIT, OCCULT, LUTIST, LOCUST, COITUS, STOUT, STOIC, STILT, SCOUT, LOTUS, ICTUS, CUTIS, CLOUT, TOUT, TOLU, TOIL, TILT, SUIT, STOT, SLUT, SLOT, SLIT, SILT, SCUT, SCOT, OUST, OTIC, LUST, LOUT, LOTI, LOST, LIST, CULT, COST, COLT, CLOT, CIST

6 **Polyword**

CLAMPDOWN, DOLMAN, COWMAN, ALMOND, WOMAN, NOPAL, NOMAD, MONAD, MODAL, DOLMA, COPAL, CLAMP, CAPON, CAMPO, WOAD, WAND, PLAN, PAWN, PAWL, PALM, OPAL, MOLA, MOAN, LOAN, LOAM, LOAD, LAWN, LAND, LAMP, DOPA, DAWN, DAMP, DAMN, COMA, COLA, CODA, COAL, CLAW, CLAP, CLAN, CLAM, CLAD, CAPO, CAMP, CALM, ALOW

7 **Polyword**

ENTRAPPED, ENDPAPER, PRETEND, PERPEND, TREPAN, TENDER, REPENT, RENTED, RAPPEN, RANTED, PENTAD, PEDANT, PARENT, PANTED, PANDER, NEPETA, NAPPER, NAPPED, ENTRAP, ENRAPT, ENDEAR, EARNED, ARDENT, APPEND, TREND, TREEN, TERNE, REDAN, RANEE, PREEN, PATEN, NAPPE, ENTER, EATEN, DENAR, TERN, TEND, TEEN, TARN, RENT, REND, RANT, RAND, PENT, PEEN, PEAN, PANT, PANE, NERD, NEEP, NEED, NEAT, NEAR, NEAP, NARD, NAPE, ERNE, EARN, DENT, DENE, DEAN, DARN, ANTE

8 **Polyword**

SCIENTIST, TINIEST, TESTIS, SENITI, NICEST, INSIST, INSETS, INSECT, INCITE, INCEST, STINT, STETS, STENT, STEIN, SCENT, INSET, TITI, TINT, TINE, TEST, TENT, STET, SNIT, SITE, SETT, SENT, SECT, NITE, NETT, NEST, CITE, CIST, CENT

9 **Polyword**

MOMENTARY, MONETARY, METONYM, ANYMORE, YEOMAN, ORNATE, NOTARY, MOMENT, MOANER, MENTOR, MEMORY, MATRON, MARMOT, ETYMON, TONER, TENOR, ROMAN, RAYON, ORATE, OATER, MORAY, MONTE, MONEY, METRO, MAYOR, MANOR, ATONE, ATOMY, YORE, TYRO, TROY, TORN, TORE, TONY, TONE, TOME, TOEA, TARO, RYOT, ROTE, ROTA, ROAN, ROAM, OMEN, NOTE, NORM, NOME, MOTE, MORT, MORN, MORE, MOAT, MOAN, MENO, MEMO, MAYO, ATOM, AMMO, AEON

10 **Polyword**

SPRIGHTLY, TRIGLYPH, RIGHTLY, GRISTLY, STRIPY, SHIRTY, RIGHTY, LYRIST, GRISLY, THRIP, STRIP, SPRIT, SPRIG, SPIRT, SHIRT, RIGHT, GRITS, GRIST, GIRTH, TRIP, TRIG, STIR, SPRY, PRIG, GRIT, GRIP, GIRT, GIRL

11 **Polyword**

LUNCHTIME, MINUTE, MINUET, INHUME, HELIUM, UNMET, MUTCH, MUNCH, MULCT, MULCH, MUCIN, MINCE, MILCH, MELIC, LUMEN, LIMEN, ILEUM, HUMIC, HILUM, CUMIN, CLIME, CHIME, TIME, THEM, NEUM, MUTE, MULE, MUCH, MITE, MINT, MINE, MILT, MILE, MIEN, MICE, METH, MENU, MELT, LIMN, LIME, ITEM, HELM, EMIT, CULM, CHUM

12 **Polyword**

CARTWHEEL, TREACLE, LEATHER, CHELATE, WHALER, WELTER, WEALTH, THALER, TERCEL, RELATE, RECTAL, LECHWE, LECHER, LATHER, HEALER, HALTER, CREWEL, CLARET, CHALET, CEREAL, CARTEL, WHEEL, WHEAL, WHALE, WELCH, TRAWL, RATEL, LEECH, LEACH, LATHE, LATER, LATCH, LARCH, HALER, ELECT, ELATE, ECLAT, CREEL, CRAWL, CLEAT, CLEAR, CHELA, ARTEL, ALTER, ALERT, WELT, WEAL, WALE, TEAL, TALE, TALC, TAEL, REEL, REAL, RALE, LEET, LEER, LECH, LATH, LATE, LACE, HERL, HEEL, HEAL, HALT, HALE, EARL, CLEW, CLAW, CELT, CARL, ALEE

13 **Polyword**

GRADUATED, GRADUATE, TRUDGED, GUARDED, GRADATE, TRUDGE, TRADED, GRATED, GRADED, DRUDGE, DATURA, DARTED, ARGUED, URGED, URATE, UDDER, TRUED, TREAD, TRADE, TARGE, RATED, RAGED, GUARD, GREAT, GRATE, GRADE, DREAD, DARED, AUGER, ARGUE, ADDER, URGE, UREA, TRUG, TRUE, TRAD, TEAR, TARE, RUED, RUDE, RUDD, REDD, READ, RATE, RAGE, RAGA, GUAR, GRAD, GEAR, GAUR, DURA, DRUG, DREG, DRAT, DRAG, DEAR, DART, DARE, AURA, AREA, AGAR

14 **Polyword**

RADIATION, RADIANT, RADIAN, ORDAIN, INROAD, ADROIT, TRIAD, RADON, RADIO, NAIAD, NADIR, INDRI, IDIOT, DROIT, DRAIN, DINAR, DANIO, AROID, ADORN, TROD, TRAD, TOAD, ROAD, RIND, RAND, RAID, NARD, NADA, DRAT, DOIT, DIRT, DINT, DATA, DART, DARN, ARID, ADIT

15 **Polyword**

RECUMBENT, CENTRUM, TUREEN, TENURE, TENREC, RETUNE, RECTUM, RECENT, NEUTER, CERMET, CENTRE, CEMENT, BURNET, UNMET, TUNER, TUBER, TRUCE, TERNE, TERCE, REBUT, METRE, METER, ERECT, ENTER, CRUET, BURNT, BRUTE, BRUNT, BERET, TURN, TUNE, TUBE, TRUE, TREE, TERN, TERM, TEEN, TEEM, RUNT, RETE, RENT, MUTE, METE, MEET, CUTE, CURT, CENT, BUNT, BRUT, BENT, BEET

16 **Polyword**

MIDWINTER, NITRIDE, MINTIER, INTERIM, WINTER, WINDER, TWINER, TINDER, REWIND, REMIND, MINTER, MINTED, MINDER, INDITE, WIDEN, TWINE, TRINE, TREND, TINED, NITRE, MIRIN, MINER, MINED, INTER, INERT, INDRI, INDIE, IMINE, DINER, DENIM, WREN, WINE, WIND, WENT, WEND, TWIN, TINE, TERN, TEND, RIND, RENT, REND, REIN, NITE, NIDE, NEWT, NERD, MINT, MINI, MINE, MIND, MIEN, MEND, INTI, DINT, DINE, DENT, DENI

17 **Polyword**

PERFUMERY, PERFUMER, PERFUMY, PERFUME, PREYER, PREFER, MURREY, FRUMPY, RUPEE, REFER, PUREE, PERRY, PEERY, MURRE, MERRY, FURRY, FRYER, FRUMP, FERRY, FEMUR, EMERY, RUMP, REEF, PYRE, PURR, PURE, PREY, PERM, PERE, PEER, MURE, MERE, FURY, FREE

18 **Polyword**

CAREFULLY, CRUELLY, CLEARLY, CAREFUL, RECALL, CULLER, CELLAR, CALLER, ULCER, LUCRE, FARCY, FARCE, FACER, CURLY, CULLY, CRUEL, CLEAR, CLARY, CELLA, YUCA, RACY, RACE, LUCE, LACY, LACE, FACE, ECRU, CURL, CURE, CULL, CLUE, CLEF, CLAY, CELL, CAUL, CARL, CARE, CALL, CALF, CAFE, ACYL, ACRE

19 **Polyword**

UNTOUCHED, UNCOUTH, NOTCHED, COUNTED, TECHNO, HUNTED, EUNUCH, DOCENT, UNDUE, UNCUT, TUNED, TENDU, TENCH, OUNCE, NOTED, NOTCH, HOUND, HONED, DUNCE, COUNT, CONTE, CONED, CENTO, UNTO, UNDO, UNCO, UDON, TUNE, TONE, THEN, TEND, ONCE, NUDE, NOTE, NODE, HUNT, HONE, DUNT, DUNE, DONE, DENT, CONE, CENT

20 **Polyword**

PORTRAYAL, PORTRAY, ROTARY, RAPTOR, RAPTLY, PORTLY, PORTAL, PATROL, PARTLY, PARROT, PARLAY, PALTRY, TOLAR, TARRY, ROYAL, POLAR, PARTY, PARRY, PAROL, LORRY, ARRAY, APART, AORTA, ALTAR, TYRO, TROY, TRAY, TRAP, TORR, TARP, TARO, RYOT, ROTA, ROPY, ROAR, RAPT, PROA, PRAY, PRAT, PORT, PART, PARR, PARA, ORRA, ORAL, LORY, ARYL, ARTY, ALAR